The Open University

U116

Environment: journeys through a changing world

Block 5
Changing China

Parts 1–3

Susan Fawssett, Dick Morris and James Warren

This publication forms part of the Open University course U116 *Environment: journeys through a changing world*. Details of this and other Open University courses can be obtained from the Student Registration and Enquiry Service, The Open University, PO Box 197, Milton Keynes MK7 6BJ, United Kingdom (tel. +44 (0)845 300 60 90; email general-enquiries@open.ac.uk).

Alternatively, you may visit the Open University website at www.open.ac.uk where you can learn more about the wide range of courses and packs offered at all levels by The Open University.

To purchase a selection of Open University course materials visit www.ouw.co.uk, or contact Open University Worldwide, Walton Hall, Milton Keynes MK7 6AA, United Kingdom for a brochure (tel. +44 (0)1908 858793; fax +44 (0)1908 858787; email ouw-customer-services@open.ac.uk).

The Open University
Walton Hall, Milton Keynes
MK7 6AA
First published 2009.

Edited and designed by The Open University.

Typeset by SR Nova Pvt. Ltd, Bangalore, India.

Printed and bound in the United Kingdom by Halstan Printing Group, Amersham.

ISBN 978 0 7492 2564 3

1.1

Contents

Part 1

On the move

Susan Fawssett

In these two examples I have been using scatter diagrams *descriptively* to give a sense of the associations between one variable, GDP per capita, and another, the percentage share of either industry or agriculture. Although this is fine for my purpose, mathematicians prefer to replace descriptive phrases like 'a general trend', 'a strong link', or 'partial association' with a range of numbers, using 0 to represent no association and 1 to represent a perfect fit. They then call this numerical association the **correlation coefficient**. In this numerical form a **positive correlation** has a value between 0 and +1, and a **negative correlation** has a value between 0 and −1. However, in addition to this specific use, correlation is also used as a descriptive word when it simply means an association. The use here of the terms 'positive' and 'negative' do not indicate that the situation it represents is good or bad. It is not a value judgement, positive just indicates that both variables increase together, negative that as one increases the other decreases.

So does the positive correlation between percentage share of industry and income per person show that industrialisation causes an increase in economic output? The answer, unfortunately, is that it is not so simple. A correlation indicates that there is an association between two variables, for example GDP per capita and share of industry, but *does not* demonstrate that one is the cause of the other. The correlation could be down to chance, or it could be that growth in income causes industrialisation. Or, as is often the case, it could be that both are responding to a third factor, such as global trade. In other words, to establish whether industrialisation causes economic growth we need to look for more evidence. This would entail looking at the limits on growth from agricultural production and the economies of scale that industrialisation offers, but these are beyond our brief here.

The phenomenal manufacturing growth in China has been steered by a very proactive government. Economic transformation has been underpinned by the change from a centrally planned, **communist economy** to a centrally co-ordinated, market economy. A communist economy is where the state owns and controls all aspects of production and exchange. A **market economy** is where buyers and sellers of goods and services, largely private individuals and companies, come together in conditions of competition. Despite still calling itself a communist state and being nominally committed to the realisation of a communist society, China has become a market economy in all but name, albeit quite different from what is experienced in most Western market economies such as the UK, USA and Germany.

Such a transformation has been steered in a novel way by Chinese leaders. Just as Roman emperors, for example Hadrian, used coinage to advertise their political programmes to the people, Deng Xiaoping (Figure 1.7), who led China from 1978 until his death in 1997 and was the architect of the reforms, used proverbs. In effect, these were slogans, or short, pithy and memorable phrases which were part of a concerted campaign to bring the

Figure 1.7 Deng Xiaoping, the key architect of China's reform programme

Chinese people along in spirit and action with the reforms. The adaptation of old Chinese proverbs, and development of new ones, has provided a useful tool for Chinese leaders to present a change in direction to the people from a non-threatening platform. They help gloss over what might be uncomfortable truths as well as being a vehicle for authorities to steer people's understanding. On the surface they are rooted in ancient wisdom, their modern manifestations giving a veneer of acceptability that few question in China. Such proverbs include the following from Deng Xiaoping, who in justifying the reforms after 1978 said, 'Poverty is not socialism. To be rich is glorious.'

This signalled to the people the new path that valued wealth. It also, more subliminally, suggested that being wealthy was more important than socialism. Another saying by Deng flags that the route by which China develops is not important, just so long as it does, glossing over the tricky question as to whether China should follow a communist or capitalist path. As Deng said, 'It doesn't matter if a cat is black or white, so long as it catches mice.'

Similarly, the saying 'Let some people get rich first' suggests that the inequalities that result from a market economy are acceptable. However, seeking to recapture China's revolutionary credentials, Deng has also said, 'Reform is China's second revolution.' The first revolution was the Chinese Revolution of 1949 when the communists came to power.

The greatest difference between the market approach in China and that in the West is the extent of government control. In the West, the market is given a fairly free hand to drive the economy, with government involvement ideally kept to a minimum (although in practice this varies from country to country – spatially, and across time – temporally). In contrast, the Chinese government very actively steers economic and social development. To some extent this is a legacy of the communist period, when government controlled every aspect of Chinese society. But the difference from communist times is that steering the economy now happens within the discipline imposed by the supply and demand mechanisms of the market. To this end, the Chinese government has encouraged rural enterprises and private business, opened the country to foreign trade and investment, and invested heavily in industry and the education of the workforce. The result, as we know, has been an unprecedented period of sustained, strong economic growth.

A further initiative the Chinese government took to enhance economic growth was to limit population growth. If an economy is growing but the population is growing at the same percentage rate, then economic growth will be cancelled out by population growth; the income per person stays the same and development will not happen. Therefore, following the economic reforms in 1978, the government introduced a 'one-child policy' in 1979 (see Box 1.1 and Figure 1.8). The one-child policy was controversial, sometimes involving forcible abortion and sterilisation of women. Moreover, it is difficult to imagine any other government having the will and commitment to introduce such a policy. But the Chinese government estimated that there would be an extra 400 million people in China without it, which would place a considerable strain on resources (BBC, 2007). The policy, and its robust enforcement, demonstrates the extraordinary control that the Chinese government is able to exercise in steering development.

Figure 1.8 The typical Chinese family of three

The direct result of the 'one-child policy' was that the fertility rate (the average number of babies born to a woman) dropped from 5.8 children in 1970 to 1.6 children at the end of the twentieth century (Wang and Mason, 2005, p. 142). While the one-child policy has led to the sex ratio becoming skewed in China, as female foetuses are aborted, it also delivers tangible health benefits for women and children. Women are freed from the burden of continuous pregnancy and its related risks of morbidity (disease) and mortality (death) (Hesketh and Zhu, 1997). Similarly, the focus on a single child has positive health and developmental outcomes for the child. Thus, the under-five mortality rate dropped from 118 in 1970, before the introduction of the one-child policy, to 22 in 2007 (UNICEF, 2009).

The one-child policy also had an indirect effect in enabling families to think more strategically about how best to maximise their life chances, and those of their only child. Families could now plan for their future with more certainty.

So we have a situation where population growth has been reduced dramatically to a situation where it is on a par with many developed countries, and economic growth has averaged 10% per year since the 1980s. What is interesting about China's extraordinary level of sustained economic growth is that it is believed to have been based primarily on increases in worker productivity (production per worker) in the early stages.

Before the reforms, most people in China lived in the countryside, on land owned by the state, producing goods and services for the state and themselves. The economy was communist in that the state controlled all production and exchange, but it was also subsistence in that most people were farmers and they produced the food they subsisted on. The reforms brought dramatic change to the countryside. Farmers were allowed to lease land from the state, and what they produced on the land could be sold. But as plots of land were quite small, this freed up family members to look for other work. Farmers began to migrate to urban areas in search of factory and construction work. As a result, their economic activity began to be incorporated in GDP figures. The state controlled all the published data, so measures such as GDP represented what the state wanted them to represent, rather than globally accepted reporting standards. Before 1978, it is likely that only that element that had been taken by the state would have been included in the country's GDP; the subsistence element would not have been counted. This is one reason why worker productivity increased, together with overall levels of productivity. An analogy would be the position of many women in the UK who choose to stay at home to raise their children rather than continuing in paid work. When they are at home caring for the children they are not considered productive, in an 'industrial sense', and their work is not counted in national GDP accounts. But when they return to paid work, this work is counted in GDP figures.

This discussion demonstrates the limitations of an indicator such as GDP, in that what is counted and what is not counted can be quite arbitrary, and is often not a good reflection of the dynamics of economic activity in a country, particularly a developing country.

The great rises in productivity can be explained not only by the way GDP is calculated, but also by the introduction of the profit motive, which has spurred people to work harder. Prior to the reforms in 1978, as long as farmers met the quota dictated by the government, they were largely left alone. There was little incentive to try new production initiatives or to exceed the quota as there was no scope for personal enrichment. The result was that productivity stagnated. With the economic reforms and the introduction of private ownership, a greater willingness to try harder and to try new things developed, as any profits could now be privately owned. It is this growing entrepreneurship which has also resulted in increases in worker productivity.

The extent of the increase in Chinese productivity is felt by us all, as high productivity leads to cheaper goods. As the 'manufacturing power house' of the world, China now produces a great number of the things we consume (Figure 1.9). A report by the New Economics Foundation and the Open University in 2007 (p. 3) makes this point forcibly:

> We are ever more clothing ourselves, furnishing our homes, watching television, listening to music, playing games with our children and even decorating our Christmas trees, courtesy of goods manufactured in China.

Figure 1.9 Container port in China from where goods are shipped to destinations around the world

Activity 1.4   Identifying Chinese-made consumer goods in your home

Look around your kitchen or sitting room. Are any of the white goods (largely kitchen appliances such as washing machines, microwaves, dishwashers, ovens) or brown goods (electrical, entertainment appliances such as televisions, hi-fi systems, CD and DVD players, cameras, computers) made in China?

Discussion

You may have made the judgement as to whether the goods were made in China or not on the basis of the brand name of the product. These may be Japanese, German or American companies. But many of them will still be made in China, and a closer examination of the item might reveal that it was indeed manufactured or assembled in China. Multinational companies have been attracted to make their products in China because of the low costs. Labour costs in China are 5% of those in high wage economies such as Germany and the USA (*Financial Times*, 2008). Other costs are also lower, such as plant rental, energy, raw materials and taxes. This means that many types of goods can be made 10–30% more cheaply in China than in countries such as Germany and the USA (*Financial Times*, 2008).

The Chinese government has actively encouraged foreign manufacturing companies to come to China because of the positive impact they have on overall economic growth in providing employment. Traditionally, China's manufacturing has been mass production of low-tech parts and products such as plastic goods, toys, and light textiles such as clothes and furniture, made using abundant labour and poor quality machinery. However, this is now changing as the Chinese government seeks to encourage diversification into sophisticated design and product development such as computers, electronic goods and cars. These higher value goods employ more sophisticated forms of organisation, design, technology and production, and demonstrate that the economy is maturing. Building on its traditional strength in low-cost production, the government is now encouraging the production of goods of greater technological complexity that will soon rival those produced in the West. Capital investment, which is investment in factories, technology, infrastructure and communications, has now become more significant in fuelling economic growth in China (Hu and Khan, 1997, pp. 1–2). Capital investment is considered the most important driver of economic growth in most economic models but China suggests a different way to launch economic growth, starting with increases in worker productivity, followed by a more capital-intensive trajectory.

Summary of Section 3

This section has considered how the Chinese government has steered development, juxtaposing China's communist past with the market present. It has shown the importance of industrialisation in facilitating economic growth, and the role of the 'one-child policy' in supporting this.

The plentiful supply of cheap, flexible and pliant labour remains an attractive factor for foreign investors. The demand for labour has been met by the flow of people from the countryside to the urban areas, particularly to the cities on the eastern seaboard. We will now look at migration, a factor enabling economic growth, in particular to the household, and individual decisions that are taken to enable this flow of people.

4 Migration enables development

The discussion above suggested that the growth in the Chinese economy has been steered by the Chinese government introducing market reforms. The reforms have also led to an increase in labour productivity. This has happened because people have been prepared to move to find paid work. So we can say that this movement of people in search of work has been a major factor in enabling development in China, and this is what this section focuses on.

4.1   Migration from the countryside to the towns and cities

Migration in China is largely the movement of rural farmers from their home village to urban areas (towns and cities) in search of non-agricultural work. This is the major flow of people. This movement from the villages to the towns and cities is called *urbanisation,* whereby the percentage of people living in urban areas grows while that living in rural areas declines. There is a long history of the Chinese government controlling people's movements around the country. Migration had been tightly controlled during the communist period by a system called 'hukou' (Box 1.2).

The 'hukou' system still exists today, but the differences between rural and urban 'hukou' are less stark. It has been successively relaxed since the start of the economic reforms in 1978, but particularly in the 1990s. The intention has been to free up labour to fuel economic output. There is a strong link between migration of labour and economic output; as labour mobility increases, economic output also increases.

Migrant labour stimulates the expansion of industries and services as migrants will work for lower wages than city residents and the vast numbers of peasants in the countryside means that there is a plentiful supply of young, flexible and exploitable people constantly moving to the urban areas looking for work. This has kept urban wage rates low, though still attractive to rural dwellers, and so restrained the costs of production. This has helped exports, and the general level of economic activity providing growth. In time, this may raise urban wage rates, but this will only increase voluntary migration, providing negative feedback that stabilises wages.

Box 1.2   'Hukou'

'Hukou' is a form of population registration that was implemented in the late 1950s. Every Chinese citizen must be registered as having either rural 'hukou' if they reside in the countryside, or urban 'hukou' if they live in a city or town. The distinction was very important during communist times as it greatly affected your life chances. A person with rural 'hukou' was destined for a hard life, working the land on state-owned, collective farms (Figure 1.10), where benefits were few and there was little opportunity for self-advancement. In stark contrast, a person with urban 'hukou' was guaranteed a range of services by the state in return for their labour: a job for life, subsidised food, housing, education, medical care, a pension and other services. A child would have the same 'hukou' status as their parents so there was little intergenerational social and economic mobility. Changing 'hukou' status was extremely difficult during communist times.

The system was rigidly enforced because it allowed the communist government to squeeze farmers to provide cheap food for the cities and cheap agricultural inputs for the manufacturing process. This allowed the government to prioritise industry to spearhead development. The system was riddled with inequality between the countryside and urban areas, as well as being very inefficient in terms of resources, time and effort used for the result.

Figure 1.10 Wheat harvesting in 1968, demonstrating labour-intensive agricultural practices in pre-reform China. The banner reads 'Revolution guarantees production'. In the foreground there is a poster of Mao to 'encourage' greater effort

The growth of migration in China has been one of the most profound changes in the country since the early 1980s. While the numbers on the move are staggering, what is more interesting is that much of this migration flow has been self-initiated. The state steers small numbers of migrants into particular segments of the economy and for these people it will provide urban 'hukou'. But the great majority of migrants move at their own risk. Rural migrants have to support themselves when in the towns and cities as migrants cannot draw on urban services and benefits because these are reserved for people with urban 'hukou'. There are therefore risks for peasants thinking of migrating, which has meant that urban administrations have not been overwhelmed with migrants. This has restricted the emergence of slums, as has happened in other poor, fast-urbanising countries such as Brazil and India. Moreover, migrants can be moved back to their home villages by the police at any time. This is what happened to many migrants in Beijing in the months running up to the Beijing Olympics in July 2008.

The links between economic growth and migration in China are complex, and there are feedback effects that both multiply and restrict the outcomes. Figure 1.11 represents the situation using a multiple cause diagram.

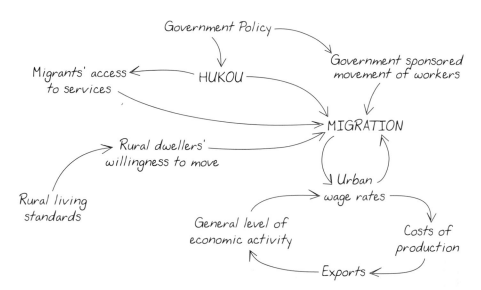

Figure 1.11 Multiple cause diagram showing the causes of migration

Key factors in Figure 1.11 are the role of 'hukou' and the willingness of rural dwellers to migrate, which in turn is strongly affected by the (low) standards of living in the countryside.

The government retains 'hukou' because it facilitates some management of population movements. It acts like an identity card system or internal passport which allows officials to tie each individual with a residence and is convenient for the purposes of the census. Moreover, it enables the state to achieve its national economic goals by providing cheap manufacturing labour. Whilst in communist times 'hukou' was perceived by most rural dwellers as a life sentence, today 'hukou' acts as a 'gatekeeper', enabling the government to enjoy the economic returns of growth in output from migrant labour without the attendant economic and social costs in terms of providing benefits and services for them in the towns and cities.

Between 1980 and 2000, as many as 268 million people moved from the Chinese countryside to the towns and cities (Yusof and Saich, 2008, p. 1). The greatest flow of migrants is east, particularly from the central region to the eastern region, but also from the western region to the eastern region (see Figure 1.4 to remind yourself how the country is divided into three economic belts). Between 1995 and 2000, the movements were over 13 million from the central to the eastern region, and close to 6 million from the western to the eastern region (Fan, 2008, p. 33).

Migration is so prevalent that it is redistributing China's population, transforming the country from a predominantly rural to an urban country. Urbanisation has transformed the spatial look of China, giving rise to more and ever bigger towns and cities (Figure 1.12). In 2007 as much as 44% of China's population lived in cities or towns, or were urbanised. This compares with a mere 19.6% of the population urbanised (less than Indonesia and India at the same time) in 1980 (Yusof and Saich, 2008, p. ix). What is so remarkable is that this profound and far-reaching change has happened in one generation. Such a large percentage growth in urbanisation is unparalleled over such a short space of time, and is reported by some to represent the largest human migration on earth.

Figure 1.12 A construction site in one of China's many expanding cities, built largely with migrant labour

Local governments, employment agencies and employers themselves actively recruit migrants in the countryside. Where particular skills are needed by employers and economic opportunities are good in distant provinces, the state steps in to sponsor migration. These people will be given urban 'hukou' at their destination. But many peasants do not have access to these channels or do not trust them, and will rely on social networks for information on job opportunities (Fan, 2008, p. 98). Other family members or villagers are seen as a reliable and trusted source of information. Moreover, they will be more likely to suggest work that they know villagers are suited to, and even to recommend them to an employer. It is not unusual to find many workers from one village working in the same factory or on the same construction site.

The profile of the typical migrant is that they are largely young, with a mean age of 27, and are more likely to be male than female (Figure 1.13). They work long hours, often based on piecework (a fixed rate is paid for each unit produced), and their wages are very low. Many foreign employers prefer to offer migrant workers dormitory accommodation and meals. The cost of food and board is deducted from their wages. This is to further control the workers' lives as it isolates them from wider society and keeps their focus on their work (Fan, 2008, p. 109).

Figure 1.13 Migrant workers laying a walkway at the approach to the Temple of Heaven in Beijing

While the majority of migrants are men, about a third are unmarried women who range in age from their late teens to late twenties. They often migrate to work in garment factories or as domestic workers and to find husbands. The fortunate few move on to more desirable and better-paid jobs in retail, restaurants, child care and office work. Sometimes married couples migrate together, but where there are children, few take them with them. Most will leave their children in the village, often with grandparents and other extended family. But when they do take their children with them, life for these migrant families is difficult, as without urban 'hukou' the family is not entitled to welfare services, including schooling for the children. This has led to the creation of migrant schools in the cities and towns, but they are poorly resourced and offer an inferior education compared with the state schools.

Migrants also experience discrimination in the highly structured labour market. As a Sichuan woman who works in a factory making spectacles said:

> We (peasant migrants) are always the front-line production workers. Better jobs like office secretaries are always reserved for the locals.
>
> *(quoted in Fan, 2008, p. 104)*

There is also a lot of resentment against the migrants from city dwellers, who argue that they steal their jobs, and accuse them of criminal acts. This is a comment frequently heard among migrants:

> When we 'waidiren'(outsiders) walk or bike we give way to the locals. They'll give you a hard time if you're not careful.
>
> *(quoted in Fan, 2008, p. 111)*

For most migrants the experience is of discriminatory treatment and harsh working conditions, and time in the city is used to earn money quickly in order to move back to the village and have a more comfortable life there. However, some migrants move to the city with the intention to settle and embrace city life. They seek new skills and education in order to make a career. These more aspirational migrants are contributing to another dimension of the Chinese economy, namely the service economy. For these migrants, city work is not just a short-term means to an end, but the realisation of a dream for a different lifestyle. You will shortly be introduced to both types of migrant through an audio programme.

4.2   Impact of migration on rural areas

During the communist period, when agriculture was organised around collectivisation/collective farms, underemployment and low productivity typified agricultural production in the countryside. Since the dismantling of the collective farms as part of the economic reforms, and the parcelling out of land to individual households on a leasehold basis, food and agricultural production have increased rapidly in the countryside. Land is allocated according to family size, and peasants are able to keep the profits from selling their produce. This has led to more efficient production, but has also freed up surplus labour. Not every household member needs to be farming the plot in order to reap the land's full potential. Consequently, households have looked to other ways to supplement and diversify their income. Sending one or more members to a town or city to work has become a common household strategy and helps to spread risk. In millions of households across China, families have sought to maximise their collective income and negotiated who should migrate in search of work.

Migrants send a large proportion of their wages back to the family in the village, leading some commentators to suggest that it has brought a rural renaissance to the Chinese countryside. Almost all remittances are spent on activities that support the collective household unit, such as house building or renovation, living expenses, farm implements and education (Fan, 2008, p. 94). Indeed, finding migrant work is seen as the main means of improving economic wellbeing in the countryside. Migration raises rural incomes, increases rural productivity and ameliorates rural poverty. Migrant households have higher incomes than non-migrant households in villages. However, this serves to increase intra-rural inequality (Fan, 2008, p. 121).

I have sought to reflect these other factors around migration in Figure 1.14 by taking the original multiple cause diagram, Figure 1.11, and adding more links.

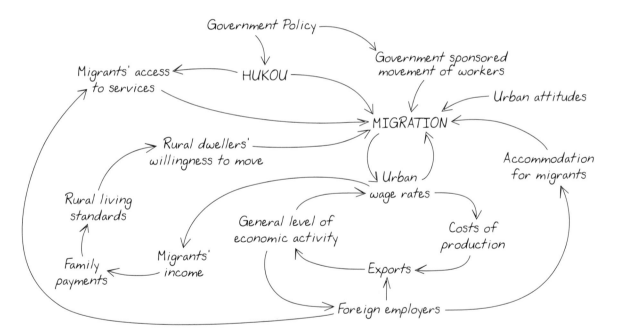

Figure 1.14 Multiple cause diagram showing the causes of migration and its impact

Migrants rarely intend to settle in the towns and cities. Returning to the village is the goal for most; as they explain, 'earn in the city and spend in the village' (Fan, 2008, p. 89). They return to the village with new skills, broadened horizons, some capital and sometimes even a spouse

(Figure 1.15). Some start new businesses, having become less risk averse from their experiences in the city, and thereby move into directly productive areas. Most migrant families hold on to their allocated farmland, leasing it if they are unable to farm it themselves. Not only is there an emotional attachment to the land, but it is also a household strategy to reduce risk. While urban employment offers the opportunity for fast money to improve rural livelihoods, land offers security and a long-term investment for the future.

Figure 1.15 Each year, millions of migrants return to their home villages to celebrate Chinese New Year with their families. As they are laden with large bags of goods and presents, it is a huge strain for China's transport infrastructure

Migration has meant a sustained increase in productivity (increased worker efficiency) in both the countryside and in the industries of the towns and cities, which many, including the International Monetary Fund, argue is the single most important factor in explaining China's phenomenal economic growth. So industrialisation coupled with migration has been the key to unleashing China's tremendous human potential.

4.3   Personal stories of migration

Shortly I will ask you to listen to an audio which tells the story of Mr and Mrs Li, who are recent migrants to Beijing, and Jackie Chu, who migrated to Beijing a number of years ago and now has urban 'hukou'. Jackie is building a career for herself in marketing. The audio demonstrates how strategic migrants are in their migration decisions and how it fits into their long-term goals. Their stories will help you to appreciate the story of transformative change in China, and how similar stories all over China are changing the spatial landscape of the country over a very short period of time.

Please listen to The Migration Story audio on the DVD. I suggest you listen all the way through the first time, and then listen again when you have read SAQ 1.2. Answer the questions after your second listening.

SAQ 1.2   Migrant stories

Mr and Mrs Li

1   List the advantages and the disadvantages of moving to Beijing for work for Mr and Mrs Li.

2   What benefits has migration brought for other migrants from the Li's home village?

3   What future do the Li family see for themselves?

Jackie

1   What factors in Jackie's background have influenced her hopes for her life in the city?

2   In what ways has Jackie's life changed?

Summary of Section 4

In this section I have looked at how migration of millions of farmers from the countryside to the towns and cities has enabled development in China, providing both a cheap source of labour for manufacturing and construction and aspirational, educated migrants for high-level services. You have heard personal testimonies from migrants about why they migrated and what life as a migrant is like, and hopefully appreciate that migrants have different aspirations regarding what they expect the city to provide. These experiences of migration may be familiar if you or your parents have made similar journeys within one country or across international borders. If so, I hope you can bring your own experience to deepen your understanding. In the next section I consider the effect of economic growth and migration, fuelled by industrialisation and urbanisation, on China's environment.

Economic growth versus the environment

5

China is paying a heavy environmental cost for its economic success. The sustainability of the country's natural resource base, the functioning and health of its ecological systems, and the health of its population have been severely compromised. China faces threats from flooding as a result of deforestation and destruction of wetlands, desertification with desert already covering one-third of the country and causing the capital, Beijing, to be shrouded in dust for days on end, water shortages as a result of increasing demand and few water conservation efforts, and dwindling forest reserves as demand for paper, furniture and chopsticks has encouraged illegal logging (Economy, 2004, pp. 9–10).

Such an environmental blacklist suggests that China's economic growth has been fuelled with little regard for the effects on the environment. But it is important to recognise that environmental degradation is an unintended consequence of economic growth, and an unwanted by-product. The fast consumption of raw materials is due not only to the rapid pace of growth, but also because of the high energy needs of China's growth path. China's major source of energy is the burning of coal (Figure 1.16), which is highly polluting, with acid rain and smog experienced locally and implications for severe climate change globally, because fossil fuel consumption (together with cement production) are the main man-made sources of the greenhouse gas CO_2 (Gregg et al., 2008, p. 1). Since 2006, China has been the largest producer of CO_2 emissions, with 54% of the global increase in CO_2 from 2001–06 coming exclusively from China (Gregg et al., 2008, p. 1).

Figure 1.16 Coal-fired power station close to a Chinese city suburb

The extent of the pollution problem became an international concern during the 2008 Beijing Olympics. The International Olympic Committee and concerned athletes were worried that the Beijing smog could pose a health hazard to athletes (Figure 1.17). It was rumoured that distance races might have to be postponed until the smog cleared and there were fears that some athletes might compete wearing face masks. In the event, distance races were not postponed, and the unedifying spectacle of athletes wearing face masks did not happen. The Beijing Olympics' legacy was their faultless operation and the record-breaking achievements of Olympians rather than the 'Smog Olympics'. In large part this was achieved by the Chinese government's initiatives to control pollution, cutting back on heavy industry in Beijing before and during the games. For example, Capital Steel, one of Beijing's worst polluters, cut production back to a mere 27% of the norm in its plant in the western suburbs of Beijing (Fletcher, 2008). This demonstrates that, when necessary, political will to curb environmental damage can be mobilised, at least in the short term.

Figure 1.17 Smog obscures the Bird's Nest, the Beijing Olympics track and field venue

Outside the special circumstances of the Olympics, China's pollution threatens the long-term health of the economy and its people. Air pollution is worst in the towns and cities, where manufacturing plants are located, but it affects the whole country. As stated earlier, almost half of China's population now lives in urban areas. A study by the Chinese Academy on Environmental Planning blamed air pollution for 411 000 premature deaths in 2003. The deaths were largely from lung- and heart-related diseases (Watts, 2005). Other health worries are the rise in cancers and birth defects, which are thought to be caused by chemical industries. It has been estimated by the government's environmental watchdog, the State Environmental Protection Administration (SEPA) that the costs inflicted by pollution amount to between 8 and 13% of GDP each year (*The Economist*, 2008a, p. 21).

Below is a short article from the BBC news website from August 2008. It considers a threat to the environment other than pollution, the damage to a rainforest in Yunnan province. This is because of the illegal cutting down of the rainforest to plant rubber trees. It demonstrates that some local people are concerned about their environment and are beginning to contest such damage. However, the article also highlights the difficulties they encounter in speaking out and the role of environmental activists in giving them a voice.

Activity 1.5   Environmental damage in Xishuangbanna forest

Read the article below and answer the following questions.

1 What is the problem?

2 Why have some farmers opted to grow rubber trees?

3 What does this article tell you about the different views about the forest?

4 What does this article tell you about conflicting attitudes and approaches to the environment in China?

5 What is being done to change villagers' attitudes to the local ecosystem?

The Rising Cost of Rubber

Roseanne Gerin

Beijing Review, 19 March 2009

Even in winter the variety of flora In Xishuangbanna in southwest China's Yunnan Province is an impressive sight to behold. The north tropical monsoon climate ensures a year-round abundance of fruit. Besides run-of-the-mill offerings such as pineapples, coconuts and bananas is more exotic fare such as papayas, tamarinds, jackfruit and mangosteens.

This tropical fruit salad is a marked contrast to the rolling brown hills with rows upon rows of tall, slender, leafless rubber trees, sticking straight out of the earth like oversized matchsticks. Early March is usually the beginning of the annual tapping season here, when a thin layer of top bark is removed along a downward half spiral on each tree to allow milky latex to drip down into a collecting cup at the base.

'Banna' as it's called by locals, is one of China's two rubber-producing areas; the other one is in Hainan Province. Although the cash crop is not native to Yunnan, it has been a mixed blessing for the local economy and ecosystem since it was introduced in the late 1940s. A few years later, the government sent researchers to the area to determine the feasibility of growing rubber as a strategic natural resource.

Beginning in the mid-1950s, the government started clearing large swathes of tropical seasonal rainforest – the only one in China – to make way for state-owned rubber plantations. Large-scale deforestation continued until the early 1980s for farmland, rubber and tropical fruit tree plantations and for timber. Today there are both state-owned and private rubber plantations. As rubber prices have tripled over the last decade, the world's largest tiremakers have gotten in on the act, forming cooperation deals for rubber research and development with state-owned companies.

Researchers at the Xishuangbanna Tropical Botanical Garden (XTBG), a conservation research institute under the Chinese Academy of Sciences, have been documenting the effects of rubber plantations on the local ecosystem for the last few decades. A study in 2006 found that about 67 percent of the tropical rainforest in Xishuangbanna had been lost to rubber plantations between 1976 and 2003. Today rubber trees cover almost 400,000 hectares, or about one fifth of Xishuangbanna Prefecture's territory, according to a recent article in the scientific journal *Nature*.

The forces of *yin* and *yang* are at work in rubber production in Xishuangbanna. As the world's largest consumer and importer of natural rubber, China has a huge appetite for latex for its booming automotive industry. The government has set a goal to produce one third more rubber, or nearly 859,800 tons, by 2010 than it did in 2007. In the meantime, scientists here are researching new strains of rubber trees that can grow at higher elevations, since most are already planted in the low-lying areas of Xishuangbanna, and how to speed up their maturity rate. The plans have the blessing of the Yunnan government, which believes it is necessary to increase natural rubber industrial development in the province.

Rubber trees have benefited the local economy tremendously, because they are one of the more lucrative cash crops for farmers to grow. They can earn net income of 15,000 yuan ($2,200) a year per hectare for rubber compared with 2,000–3,000 yuan ($292–$438) for rice or tea, according to *Nature*.

But the expansion of rubber production will continue to come at the expense of the area's ecosystem, which XTBG researchers say has quickly deteriorated during the last 10 years as demand for rubber has soared. The rubber trees suck up huge amounts of water, cause soil erosion and reduce the area's biodiversity. The pesticides used on the trees run off into local water supplies used by villages. Ecologists also believe that deforestation is partly responsible for an overall temperature increase in the area.

The most concern has come from the XTBG, which ironically got its start from the government's efforts to plant rubber trees here. In recent years, researchers have suggested that the government limit new rubber plantations to land currently used for other crops.

Local officials in Xishuangbanna Prefecture have taken notice. Last month, they were hammering out a regulatory plan to restore the area's ecosystem, increase controls over forestland in protected corridors, and restore others in buffer zones of national nature reserves that have been converted to rubber farms, according to *Nature*.

But such plans could have little impact, because the commodity's high demand and price will continue to be the main incentives for farmers and state-owned enterprises to grow rubber trees. Meanwhile, the Asian Development Bank has stepped in with a pilot project that seeks to increase villagers' ecological awareness and help them better manage their land. The project also provides microcredit funds to villagers in the Greater Mekong Subregion, including Xishuangbanna, if they set up new protected zones in their areas.

Gerin, R. (2009) 'The Rising Cost of Rubber', *Beijing Review*, 19 March, p. 48.

Discussion

1 The problem is the cutting down of the rainforest to plant rubber trees, which damages the ecosystem of the area as a result of soil erosion, toxic run-off into water supplies and temperature increase.

2 Some farmers have opted to chop down the rainforest and plant rubber trees because rubber prices have tripled over the last decade and far outstrip what can be made by growing other crops, such as rice and tea.

3 Researchers at the Xishuangbanna Tropical Botanical Garden (XTBG) want to preserve the rainforest and local officials of the Xishuangbanna Prefecture are also putting in place measures to try to restore the area's ecosystem. But farmers and state owned enterprises are likely to continue to grow rubber because of the high demand and price for the commodity.

4 The article demonstrates the conflicting interests around the rainforest and different values placed on the functions of the rainforest. Growing rubber leads to a quick financial return for the growers and contributes to meeting the needs of the Chinese economy for the commodity. The adverse effects on the ecosystem are subordinated to this. But this local contradiction between economic growth and the environment is symbolic of the bigger contradiction that is played out across China, and indeed, many fast-developing countries.

5 The Asian Development Bank is piloting a project to build villager's skills and knowledge in managing their land in a more ecologically aware manner

Thus, this article demonstrates that environmental destruction is being contested by some groups. I will now look at how China's environmental damage is being more widely contested.

Summary of Section 5

This section has considered the conflict between the rush for economic growth in China and the damage this has caused to China's environment, its contribution to global warming, and the changed land-use patterns it has generated. It has also briefly engaged with the diverse perspectives on the environment in China, which is further explored in the next section.

6 Environmental groups contest environmental degradation

The public action model introduced earlier demonstrates that the steering of development by the government and enabling of development by the migration of millions of people has had profound environmental damage. The focus on economic growth means that industrial output is valued above 'non-material services' such as fresh air and clean water. But this does not go unchallenged. Many in Chinese society are unhappy with China's development path, particularly the environmental destruction it has brought in its wake. Some people have felt sufficiently agitated to join environmental non-governmental organisations (NGOs), which are seeking to bring about a change in attitudes to encourage greater protection of the environment.

Environmental groups are a fairly new phenomenon in China. The first group, 'Friends of Nature', was formed in 1994, and protested against the loss of biodiversity. It worked with the Chinese media, and by means of education campaigns began to increase the Chinese people's awareness of environmental issues. Championing biodiversity was a safe topic as it did not directly criticise government and was therefore tolerated. But by the late 1990s Chinese environmental NGOs began to be more assertive. A successful and energetic lawyer, Wang Canfa, established the Centre for Legal Assistance to Pollution Victims. This organisation prosecuted environmental pollution cases on behalf of pollution victims and represented a more confrontational approach in contesting environmental degradation. Pan Yue, a deputy minister at the SEPA, records that the environment is the second most popular subject for popular protests after land disputes (Figure 1.18), with 50 000 protests in

Figure 1.18 Pollution protest in Beijing

2005, which represented a 30% increase on the previous year (*The Economist*, 2008a, p. 22).

In 2006 there were over 6000 registered environmental groups in China (*The Economist*, 2008b). They are growing in number and also in influence, informing and educating widely on environmental issues. The Chinese government, the judiciary, the media, the business sector and the fast-expanding Chinese middle class are increasingly expressing concern about the environmental impacts of rapid growth, in particular the energy-inefficient and dirty processes being used. Moreover, there is an emerging awareness that the environmental consequences of rapid economic growth could actually undermine the phenomenal development already achieved.

However, just how these concerns can be mobilised for action presents huge challenges. There are many hurdles to be surmounted, including galvanising political will amongst local officials, building their administrative capacity to effect change and committing sufficient finance to the problem by central government.

The political inertia around environmental issues that characterised many regional governments is a major problem. Regional officials believe that as long as they are delivering on economic growth targets without too much local protest, they can expect to be considered favourably for promotion by central government regardless of how polluted and degraded their regions are (*The Economist*, 2008b). Moreover, they often have close ties with the local businesses and factories that cause the pollution and degradation, which further compromises their willingness to act (Economy, 2004, p. 20).

Central government has tried a range of strategies to encourage officials to take environmental pollution more seriously, including revoking honorary titles, ruining career prospects, and naming and shaming offenders. However, many officials remain resistant to change (Graham-Harrison, 2008). As Zhang Lijun, another deputy minister at SEPA, laments, 'Some of the policies put forward by the central government, when they are implemented at the local level, in some places they are not completed or in place' (Graham-Harrison, 2008). Central government has also tried to punish polluting companies by banning them from listing on the stock market, suspending their operations or shutting them down.

One of China's most notorious recent environmental disasters highlights the effects of political inertia and lack of administrative capacity. In 2007 the choking of the country's third largest freshwater lake, Taihu, by a toxic algal bloom led to water supplies being contaminated for several days for over 2 million people (Figure 1.19). It sparked panic hoarding of bottled water as an alternative water supply and led China's premier, Wen Jiabao, to say, 'The pollution of Taihu Lake has sounded the alarm for us.' While he went on to call for co-operation between central and local governments, and for

Figure 1.19 The shoreline of Lake Taihu at the height of an algal bloom

Indeed, environmental NGOS have also been a key axis around which people have begun to learn how to contest government policy more broadly. Political power in China is highly centralised and the level of control exercised by the government over the huge population is intense. Fearing any form of dissent, the government exercises heavy censorship. Its agreement with the search engine company Google to censor access within China to the World Wide Web is an example of the control over information that the government exercises. What this means is vividly demonstrated in Figure 1.21, where the results of two Google image searches in 2008 for the term 'Tiananmen Square' are displayed. Tiananmen Square is the major square in Beijing and it is where democracy protests took place in 1989 in which several hundred citizens were shot dead by the Chinese army. The first image is from Google Images and the second from Google Images China.

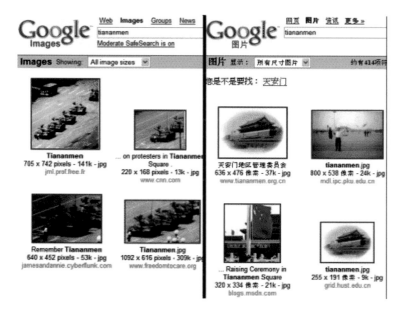

Figure 1.21 Comparison of Google searches in the West and in China demonstrating censorship in China

Similarly, the banning of Falun Gong, a spiritual group which has a reputed 70 million members in China (Wikipedia, 2009) is because of its cohesiveness and ability to mobilise its members rather than because of its philosophy. Freedom House, an American NGO that publishes an annual report on the degree of democratic freedoms in countries as measured on a scale from 1 (most free) to 7 (least free), scored China at 7 for political rights and 6 for civil liberties in 2008 (Freedom House, 2008).

Environmental politics in China are encouraging public action and addressing people's grievances. The environment is a relatively safe issue about which to become politically aware and active. But as the examples of the censorship of Google and banning of Falun Gong demonstrate, there is little tolerance of calls for greater democracy or human rights. But environmental politics could be helping to build a more active *civil society*. Civil society is the arena where people come together to pursue shared interests, purposes and values. It embraces a variety of actors, but most commonly charities, NGOs, community groups, faith-based organisations and business associations. It largely operates in the space between the economy (the market) and the state (government). It is an instrument to inject the interests of people and society into a dialogue with the market and state around how society is governed. How far a young civil society will open up Chinese politics is being keenly watched both within China and beyond.

Activity 1.6   Critical evaluation of environmental NGOs in China

As environmental action in China is a fast evolving area, I would like you to build a more current understanding of their activities. Below are three NGOs that are very active as I write in 2009, and I hope will have an enduring presence. I would like you to visit the website of one of them and spend a little time researching their activities and campaigns and then answer the questions.

Choose one of the three NGOs below and then answer the questions.

1   Friends of Nature, China (you need to put the word China into the search engine as there is another non-Chinese organisation with the same name)

2   Global Village Beijing

3   Global Environment Institute, China

Questions

1   What are the aims of the NGO you looked at?

2   List and/or briefly describe some of the programmes the NGO is involved in.

3   How does the NGO engage the public and media in its activities?

Discussion

1   I looked at Friends of Nature, China (FON), the country's oldest environmental NGO. Its aims were to promote awareness among the public of environmental concerns and to protect the environment.

2   Their campaigns are:

    to protect the Tibetan antelope and the snub-nosed monkey

    the 26°C air-conditioning energy-saving campaign, where people are encouraged to turn their air conditioning down

    'Beijing for Bikes' – organised cycle rides around the city to encourage people to use bikes more.

3   FON are producing a newsletter and commissioning and publishing books on environmental issues to engage the public and media. They have produced environmental education curriculum materials that are used by teachers across China and run environmental activity volunteer clubs for young people, such as bird watching, botany and mountain hiking. This is in recognition that young people can be effective agents of change with their parents on environmental issues. FON are training people to start their own grassroots environmental NGOs, thereby spreading good

Answers to SAQs

SAQ 1.1

The literacy rate was 66% in 1982, and 91% in 2000.

SAQ 1.2

Mr and Mrs Li

Question 1

Advantages	Disadvantages
Improved living standards	Poor housing
Can live together	Discrimination
Have heat in winter, air conditioning in summer	Hard work
Eat more meat	Difficult to get water
Earn £10 a day combined	Polluted and dusty air
	Health suffering
	High cost of living
	Little leisure time

Question 2

Villagers have electricity, TV, DVDs, electric bicycles, washing machines, indoor toilet.

Question 3

Mr and Mrs Li do not want to stay in Beijing. They envisage returning to the village and retaining their acre of land. Perhaps they will return after they have paid for their son's marriage.

Jackie

Question 1

Had 2 sisters when one-child policy

Five-room brick house

Mother a school teacher

Mother aspirational for her

Got to university

Question 2

Owns apartment

Soft furnishings

Eats out a lot

Air con, natural gas

Travels in taxis

Has credit card

Buys beautiful things she doesn't need

Buys personal care products

References

BBC (2007) 'Has China's one-child policy worked?', 20 September, http://news.bbc.co.uk/1/hi/world/asia-pacific/7000931.stm (Accessed 20 July 2009).

Chandler, C., Levinstein, J. and Zhang Dahong (2004) 'Inside the new China: part communist, part capitalist – and full speed ahead', *Fortune*, 4 October.

CIA (2009) *The World Factbook*, https://www.cia.gov/library/publications/the-world-factbook/geos/CH.html (Accessed 11 February 2009).

Economy, E.C. (2004) *The River Runs Black: the Environmental Challenge to China's Future*, Ithaca, New York, Cornell University Press.

Fan, C. (2005) 'Modeling interprovincial migration in China, 1985–2000', *Eurasian Geography and Economics*, vol. 46, no. 3, pp.165–84.

Fan, C. (2008) *China on the Move*, Abingdon, Routledge.

Financial Times (2008) 'China's new formula. Manufacturers begin to move beyond low cost', 29 May.

Fletcher, M. (2008) 'Giant steelworks' leap lets Beijing breathe in time for the Olympics', *Times Online*, 19 July, http://www.timesonline.co.uk/tol/sport/olympics/article4360253.ece (Accessed 4 June, 2009).

Freedom House (2008) *China Country Profile*, http://www.freedomhouse.org/template.cfm?page=363&year=2008 (Accessed 2 June 2009).

Graham-Harrison, E. (2008) 'China says pollution goals low as unveils ministry', *Reuters*, 11 March, http://www.reuters.com/article/latestCrisis/idUSPEK293768 (Accessed 11 April 2009).

Gregg, J., Anders, R. and Marland, G. (2008) 'China: emissions pattern of the world leader in CO_2 emissions from fossil fuel consumption and cement production', *Geophysical Research Letters*, vol. 35, LO8806.

Harrabin, R. (2007) 'China building more power plants', BBC online, 19 June, http://news.bbc.co.uk/1/hi/world/asia-pacific/6769743.stm (Accessed 20 May 2009).

Hesketh, T. and Zhu, W. (1997) 'Health in China: the one child family policy: the good, the bad, and the ugly', *British Medical Journal*, vol. 314, p.1685, http://www.bmj.com/cgi/content/full/314/7095/1685 (Accessed July 2009).

Hu, Z. and Khan, M. (1997) *Why is China Growing So Fast?*, Washington DC, International Monetary Fund, http://www.imf.org/EXTERNAL/PUBS/FT/ISSUES8/issue8.pdf (Accessed 4 June 2009).

Maddison, A. and Wu, H.X. (n.d.) 'China's economic performance: how fast has GDP grown; how big is it compared to the USA?', University of Groningen, http://www.ggdc.net/Maddison/articles/China_Maddison_Wu_22_Feb_07.pdf (Accessed 17 September, 2009).

New Economics Foundation and the Open University (2007) *Chinadependence. The Second UK Interdependence Report*, London, New Economics Foundation.

Pan Yue (2007) 'Green China and young China', *China Dialogue*, 17 July, http://www.chinadialogue.net/article/show/single/en/1167-Green-China-and-young-China-part-one (Accessed 31 January 2009).

The Economist (2008a) 'China's quest for resources', Special Report, 13 March.

The Economist (2008b) 'Environmental protection in China', 24 January.

UNICEF (2009) *China: Country statistics, 2009*, http://www.unicef.org/infobycountry/china_statistics.html (Accessed 9 April 2009).

United Nations (2008) *UNGASS Progress Report, P.R. China, Reporting period January 2006–December 2007*, http://data.unaids.org/pub/Report/2008/china_2008_country_progress_report_en.pdf (Accessed 9 April 2009).

United States Congress (2005) *Environmental NGOs in China: Encouraging action and addressing public grievances. Roundtable before the Congressional-Executive Commission on China, February 7, 2005*, http://frwebgate.access.gpo.gov/cgi-bin/getdoc.cgi?dbname=109_house_hearings&docid=f:20182.wais (Accessed 11 April 2009).

Wang, F. and Mason, A. (2005) 'Demographic dividend and prospects for economic development in China', Proceedings of the United Nations Expert Group Meeting on Social and Economic Implications of Changing Population Age Structures, Mexico City, 2005, p. 142, http://www.un.org/esa/population/meetings/Proceedings_EGM_Mex_2005/wang.pdf (Accessed 23 September 2009).

Watts, J. (2005) 'Satellite data reveals Beijing as air pollution capital of the world', *The Guardian*, 31 October, http://www.guardian.co.uk/news/2005/oct/31/china.pollution (Accessed 20 July 2009).

Wikipedia (2009) 'Falun Gong', http://en.wikipedia.org/wiki/Falun_Gong (Accessed 20 July 2009).

World Bank (2006) *Gender Gaps in China: Facts and Figures*, http://siteresources.worldbank.org/INTEAPREGTOPGENDER/Resources/Gender-Gaps-Figures&Facts.pdf (Accessed 9 April 2009).

World Bank (2009a) Call for a Green China: Conference and Cultural Event on Sustainable Development, http://web.worldbank.org/WBSITE/EXTERNAL/COUNTRIES/EASTASIAPACIFICEXT/CHINAEXTN/0,,contentMDK:21219556~isCURL:Y~menuPK:318956~pagePK:64027988~piPK:64027986~theSitePK:318950,00.html (Accessed 12 March 2009).

World Bank (2009b) 'China. World Bank urges broadening of China's poverty reduction agenda', http://web.worldbank.org/WBSITE/EXTERNAL/COUNTRIES/EASTASIAPACIFICEXT/CHINAEXTN/0,,contentMDK:22131892~pagePK:1497618~piPK:217854~theSitePK:318950,00.html (Accessed 9 April 2009).

Young, N. (2007) 'How much inequality can China stand?', Special Report from *China Development Brief*, 26 February, http://www.chinadevelopmentbrief.com/node/1001 (Accessed 22 July 2009).

Yusuf, S. and Saich, T. (2008) *China Urbanizes. Consequences, Strategies and Policies*, Washington DC, The World Bank.

Part 2
Feeding China

Dick Morris

Introduction

Part 2 of this block examines the question of how the huge Chinese population has been fed during the last century, and how this is changing, with potentially large implications for the rest of the world. It will also provide you with some basic ideas about nutrition and the environmental consequences of different ways of feeding humankind.

Sections 2–5 look at the early twentieth century Chinese rural diet, to compare and contrast it with modern European diets in terms of composition and nutritional adequacy. The production methods used are then examined, to consider how crop nutrients are supplied, the (limited) role of livestock in that system, and its environmental impact. The sections also touch on the political organisation of agriculture, and the changes (for better and worse) during the Mao era.

Sections 6–8 consider the recent changes that have occurred with increasing urbanisation and growing prosperity. These include increased use of fertilisers and industrially produced inputs to agriculture, along with increased consumption of meat, especially in the cities. The consequences of this in terms of overall food production and trade are examined. This gives a wider picture of the factors affecting land use and food production efficiency, including some basic economics and animal nutrition.

Sections 9 and 10 allow you to consider the wider implications of changing diets, and what can be done to minimise any environmental damage caused by 'Westernised urban' diets.

2 Feeding China's millions

You should by now have some feeling for the vast area of China and its large, increasingly mobile, population. What you may not have appreciated is that much of the surface area of China is at high altitude, dry and inhospitable (Figure 2.1(a) and (b)), so that crop growing is only possible on a relatively limited area (Figure 2.2).

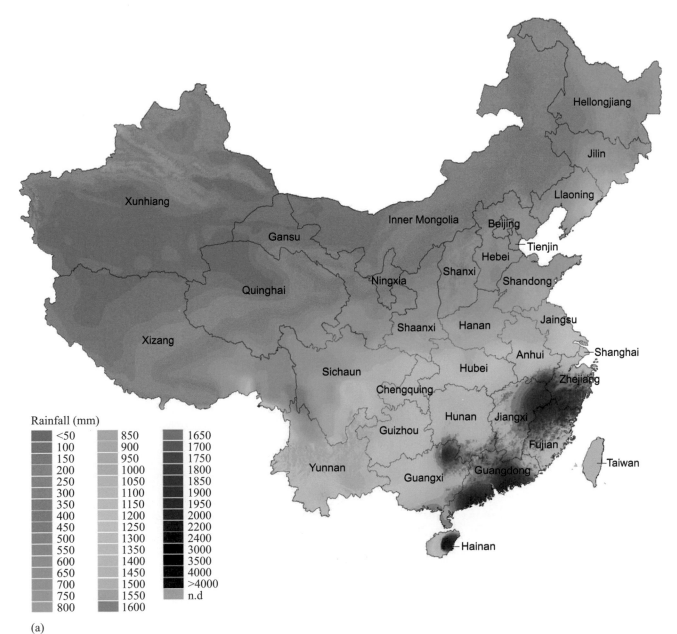

Rainfall (mm)

<50	850	1650
100	900	1700
150	950	1750
200	1000	1800
250	1050	1850
300	1100	1900
350	1150	1950
400	1200	2000
450	1250	2200
500	1300	2400
550	1350	3000
600	1400	3500
650	1450	4000
700	1500	>4000
750	1550	n.d
800	1600	

(a)

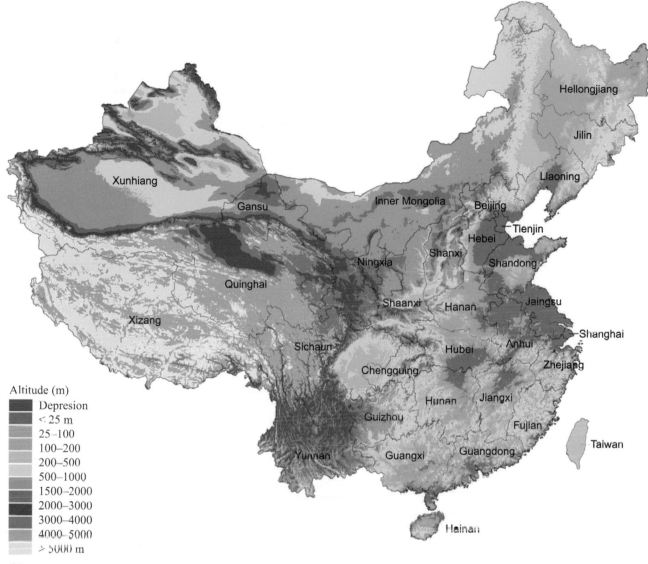

Altitude (m)

Depresion
< 25 m
25–100
100–200
200–500
500–1000
1500–2000
2000–3000
3000–4000
4000–5000
> 5000 m

(b)

Figure 2.1 China's rainfall (a) and altitude (b). *Source: Heilig (1999)*

Given these limitations, feeding the Chinese population has always been problematic, and this has resulted in the particular characteristics of the traditional Chinese diet. To consumers in Europe, the term 'Chinese food' probably conjures up images of the intriguing flavours and variety suggested by Table 2.1, compiled from a variety of typical menus found around south-east England.

Table 2.1 illustrates the wide range of different items typical of this cuisine. Meat comes as chicken, beef, duck, lamb and seafoods such as prawns. There is a range of vegetables: beans, beansprouts, mangetout (a French name for a form of peas!), and the undefined 'mixed vegetables'.

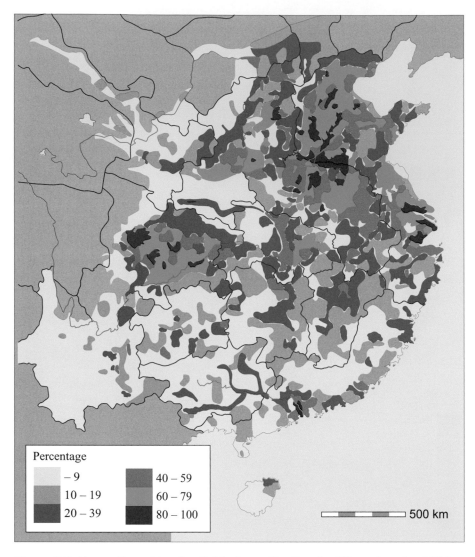

Figure 2.2 Proportion of land suitable for cultivation in different parts of China in the early twentieth century. *Source: Buck (1937)*

Green peppers and chilli add different flavours, as do the various sauces. We probably take for granted the rice. In food science, this and items such as the pancakes are called *staples* which, as you will see below, may provide a major part of our dietary needs. In reality, the menu in Table 2.1 represents the cuisine of just one particularly affluent area in the south-east of China, Guandong (previously anglicised as Canton). This area includes the port of Hong Kong, which became a British-controlled territory after the Opium Wars of 1839–1860, so it was easy for local Chinese people to emigrate to Britain, where they discovered there was a ready market for their style of cooking. For the vast majority of the Chinese population, until

Table 2.1 Some typical menu items from Chinese restaurants in England

Set meal for 2 people

Chicken and Sweetcorn Soup

Spring Pancake Roll and Satay Chicken served on Cocktail Sticks

Sizzling Beef with Black Bean and Green Pepper

Sweet and Sour Chicken Cantonese Style

Sauteed Mangetout with Beansprouts

Egg Fried Rice

Set meal for 4 people

Mixed Hors D'oeuvre

Sizzling Lamb in Satay Sauce

Sweet and Sour Pork Cantonese Style

Fried Chicken with Fresh Mushrooms and Chinese Mushrooms in Oyster Sauce

Fried Mixed Vegetables

Egg Fried Rice

Set meal for 4 people

Mixed Hors D'oeuvre

Crispy Aromatic Szechuan Duck (served with Pancakes and Hoi Sin Sauce)

Stir Fried Finely Shredded Beef with Chilli

Sizzling Sliced Lamb with Black Bean and Green Pepper

Sweet and Sour King Prawns Cantonese Style

Mange Tout and Beansprouts

Special Fried Rice

recently the typical diet was very different from the Cantonese form. You should recall from the 'Migration' audio the sorts of food consumed by the migrant workers and by Jackie's parents, which had changed little throughout preceding centuries.

2.1 Traditional Chinese diets

In the 1920s, three-quarters of China's then 150 million households lived on their mainly rented family farms, which provided an average of over 80% of their food (Croll, 1983). The 15–20% of food consumed by rural agrarian households that was not home produced was bought in local markets supplied either by those who had surplus local products or from regions of China with more favourable growing conditions. Money to buy food was earned by working for other landholders or in small local industries such as building or metalworking. Urban dwellers who could not grow enough within their own boundaries to feed themselves were largely dependent on local food markets supplied from the surrounding countryside. There was limited inter-regional trade, mainly in rice from the Lower Yangtze river basin.

Table 2.2 shows the make-up of average rural Chinese diets in the 1920s, taken from a study by J.L. Buck, an American agricultural economist who examined food production in seventeen localities and seven provinces in northern and eastern China. The data quoted are averages across all his study areas and are therefore not representative of a particular community.

Table 2.2 Proportion of total food energy obtained from different foodstuffs in China 1922–25	
Food source	**Percentage of total food energy supplied by that component**
Seeds and seed products	89.8*
Roots	8.5
Animal products	1.0
Vegetables	0.4
Sugar	0.2
Fruit	0.1

Source: Buck, 1930. *In a version of this table in Croll (1983) this value was quoted as 92.8 so that the percentages did not sum to 100. This is always a danger in using secondary sources

The categories used in Table 2.2 refer to the original forms of the different foods. Seeds and seed products includes the seeds of the cereals rice, wheat and maize, usually eaten boiled or as breads. Another group of seeds is the beans such as soya. Tofu or bean curd, manufactured from soya beans, was the Chinese equivalent of milk-derived cheese for Europeans. Familiar roots included carrots, beetroot and parsnips, but in Buck's study the main root was sweet potato. Vegetables included onions, various members of the Brassica (cabbage) family such as Chinese cabbage, and of the cucumber family (cucurbits) such as squash. Figure 2.3 shows a representative selection of these materials.

The apparent obvious difference between Tables 2.1 and 2.2 is the predominance of seeds and seed products and the tiny amount of meat in the latter. However, we need to be careful about jumping to such a conclusion without looking at the units used in the table. Table 2.2 gives the proportions of the different components in terms of the *food energy* that they supply (Box 2.1). We need to check that the data for food energy is a reasonable proxy (Block 2) for the more familiar weight or volume by which we judge the amounts of food we eat. Table 2.3 gives an indication of the variation in the food energy per 100 g for a range of different foodstuffs.

Figure 2.3 Some typical food plants: (a) rice; (b) soya bean; (c) sweet potato; (d) Chinese cabbage; (e) gourd; (f) maize; (g) wheat

Box 2.1   Food energy

Humans need food to supply energy, *protein* and a number of other essential components in order just to survive. Crucially, we also need water, since we cannot survive more than a few days without it, but this is not normally regarded as a food. The next priority for survival is food energy; under extreme conditions of starvation, our bodies have to break down first their stored body fats, then even the proteins in muscle tissue, in order to provide energy to survive. You may have encountered the term 'calorie' being used as a synonym for food energy; most popular writing about food and nutrition still uses this, but the calorie is not an SI unit. Recall from earlier blocks that the SI unit of energy is the joule (J), or its multiples kilojoules (kJ, 1000 J) and megajoules (MJ, 10^6 J) – it is kJ that appears on most food information. One calorie is exactly the same as 4.2 joules, so the conversion should be easy, but there is a potential source of confusion. Many foods have their energy quoted in Calories, with a capital C, which is actually a kilocalorie, or 1000 calories. Confusingly, writers sometimes fail to capitalise the C, making their meaning unclear. To avoid this and for consistency, I will use the SI units exclusively in this text. To give you a feeling for these units, a typical European needs around 11 megajoules of food energy per day. The exact amount needed depends on various things, including body weight. As a general rule, average rural Chinese in the 1920s were considerably smaller than current Europeans, and might only need 6–8 MJ per day.

Table 2.3 Food energy per 100 g for some different foodstuffs

Food material	Energy content (kJ per 100 g)
White bread	990
Boiled potato	340
Haricot beans	1150
Cabbage	32
Pork chop	1380

Data derived from McCance and Widdowson's The Composition of Foods, 1978

Robert McCance and his scientific partner Elsie Widdowson (who died aged 93 in 2003) were responsible for formulating UK food rationing during World War. When the British population was living on their recommended wartime diet of mainly bread, vegetables and potatoes, they were probably healthier than ever, before or since.

Beans are a typical seed, and bread is mostly wheat, another seed. Both these have around 1000 kJ per 100 g. Meat, as represented by the pork chop, has more energy per 100 g, while cabbage and potatoes have much less. So the data in Table 2.2 does give a reasonable representation of the weight or volume of the different foodstuffs that would be consumed, except for vegetables and to a lesser extent roots, where the amount consumed would be even larger than is suggested by the energy data.

The two seeds dominating Table 2.2 were rice in the south of the country and wheat further north, eaten boiled, steamed, ground into a gruel or made into bread or noodles. Rice and wheat-based food such as noodles and boiled rice were called *fan* (饭) in Chinese and were eaten at every meal. Indeed, the word *fan* originally meant food. Other components of the diet were collectively known as *cai* (菜) and were used to provide some variety of taste and texture. Without *cai*, the diet would have been regarded as tasteless, but without *fan*, it was said an individual would not be full.

In fact, many traditional diets exhibit this two-component pattern, with a staple (in Europe, usually bread, potatoes or pasta; cassava, encountered in Block 4, is another) that supplies the bulk of the diet and of food energy, and a whole range of other components (meat, vegetables, herbs and spices) referred to as *taste* that are eaten in much smaller quantities. You may be able to think of examples of this staple-plus-taste formula from your own area and circumstances. The traditional British 'meat and two veg', and the ubiquitous burger and chips, don't really fit this model, since the emphasis is on the meat, rather than the staple veg. An even more extreme example is provided by the Inuit in the Arctic. The majority of their traditional diet was meat and fish, with very small amounts of plant material, showing that humans can adapt to quite different diets according to circumstances.

In the rice-eating areas of China at the time of Buck's study, breakfast would typically comprise rice gruel with mustard leaves, dried root vegetable chips or salted vegetables. The midday meal would again be rice and vegetables plus possibly vegetable soup, and the evening meal rice with salted or leftover vegetables from earlier meals, occasionally with a small amount of meat. People in the northern provinces fared rather less well, often having only two meals per day. Breakfast was a soup made from mixed cereals, possibly with coarse bread and some vegetables for taste. The midday meal was usually a form of pasta made from various ground seeds and sweet potato. In summer, after harvest, they might have a third, evening meal similar to that at midday, but with a greater variety of vegetables: onions, spinach, aubergines, peppers, cucumbers and leeks.

Buck's study took place in the 1920s, but even towards the end of the twentieth century, rural diets were not much changed. Figure 2.4 shows a welcome banquet prepared for visitors to a rural Chinese village in the 1990s, and to European eyes this probably still looks quite frugal. A personal view of Chinese food at that time is given by the author of Part 1:

> In 1985 I backpacked around China. As a Western woman, alone, I was quite a novelty, stared at in an interested way and when stationary on a train or boat, approached by people eager to practise their English. Such encounters were always good natured and I never felt in danger or threatened throughout my travels in China despite the fact that I knew no more than a dozen Chinese words and phrases, there were no signs in English and I was pretty clueless about the country.

My only negative memory of China was the food. I have never had such appalling Chinese food as in China. To this day my palate is scarred by the experience so I will always try to steer meals out with friends away from eating Chinese! Travelling on a shoestring I frequented local or midrange restaurants which were always largely empty, as very few Chinese could afford to eat out then. And yet there was an abundance of staff buzzing round rather inefficiently, reflecting the cheapness of labour. But the food was horrible. Every meal I ate, regardless of what I ordered, was the colour of bamboo shoots, an insipid, cloudy yellow. The sauce was gloopy and woolly, liquid porridge and ever so bland. There was no crisp bite to any of the vegetables because they had been overcooked. Indeed, it was two weeks of eating to live rather than eating for pleasure.

Figure 2.4 Welcoming banquet for visitors to a rural village in 1990s

Susan's unfamiliarity with the country may have meant that she was not able to get the best food available, but the point is still valid.

To examine the implications of the Chinese diet, we need briefly to consider humans' basic nutritional requirements. I have already mentioned the need for food energy, but other essential components are proteins, *minerals, vitamins* and essential fats. Table 2.4 shows the average energy and protein recommendations for humans of different ages and activity patterns, while Table 2.5 lists the energy and protein content of some typical foodstuffs. Using tables like these, it is possible to examine the adequacy of a given diet, or to construct a suitable diet for an individual. As an example, a typical European needing 11 MJ of food energy per day would need to consume just over a kilogram of bread (a large loaf) per day. This would also supply more than enough protein, but would lack several other important components.

Table 2.4 Recommended daily intake of energy in megajoules and protein in grams for European conditions

Individual	Age	Activity	Energy (MJ per day)	Protein (g per day)
Infant	0–1		3.3	20
Child	1–3		5.5	28
	3–7		7.1	40
	7–9		8.8	49
Male	9–12		10.5	63
	12–15		11.7	70
	15–18		12.6	75
	Adult	Sedentary	11.1	67
		Very active	15.1	74
		Retired	9.3	57
Female	9–12		9.6	58
	12–15		9.6	58
	15–18		9.6	58
	Adult	Sedentary	9.0	53
		Very active	10.5	63
		3–9 months pregnant	10.0	60
		Lactating	11.3	68
	55–75		8.6	50

Derived from Mottram, 1979

Activity 2.1 Basic nutritional needs

(a) What does Table 2.4 tell you about the factors affecting the energy and protein needs of a human?

(b) Identify three items in Table 2.5 that provide a lot of energy per 100 g and those that provide a lot of protein per unit consumed.

Discussion

(a) An obvious feature is that the amount of energy and protein needed increases as children grow to adulthood. This is largely a reflection of their increasing body size, and this same factor is largely responsible for the difference in energy and protein needs between males and females. For adults, activity pattern affects energy need, with a sedentary adult needing less nutrient than an active one. Lactation and, to a lesser extent, pregnancy, increases an adult female's need for energy and protein compared with her sedentary equivalent.

(b) The items that provide the highest energy density are vegetable oil and butter, followed by cheese, along with most meat/fish products and, to a lesser extent, bread. Butter and vegetable oil are almost pure *fats* (technically known as *lipids*), which have an energy density of 38 MJ per kg. (The other two major chemical components of foodstuffs are carbohydrates and proteins, both of which have energy densities of 12 MJ per kg). Cheese and meat products generally contain significant amounts of lipid, which accounts for their relatively high energy density.

The highest protein contents are found in the meats, such as pork, chicken and bacon, and cheese, followed by beans and, to a lesser extent, bread.

Table 2.5 The typical energy and protein composition of a range of foodstuffs per 100 g of the material

Foodstuff	Energy (MJ)	Protein (g)
White bread	991	7.8
Noodles	499	4.2
Wholemeal flour	1351	13.2
Boiled white rice	522	2.2
Dumpling	885	2.9
Boiled potato	343	1.4
Sweet potato	363	1.1
Cabbage	40	1.3
Turnip	60	0.7
Mung beans	447	6.4
Green beans	83	1.9
Yogurt	350	5
Cheese	1500	25
Egg	600	12.3
Beefburger	1099	20.4
Lean pork	945	32.3
Chicken	621	25
Bacon (fried)	1926	25
Cod	400	21
Apple	151	0.2
Banana	337	1.1
Butter	3041	0.4
Vegetable oil	3700	trace

Derived, with modifications, from McCance and Widdowson's The Composition of Foods, 1978

In addition to energy and protein, humans also need other components for an adequate diet, and a very narrow diet is likely to be deficient in these. Thus, green vegetables often contain high levels of particular vitamins or minerals that may be lacking in cereals. Fruits contain important vitamins and antioxidants that have recently been recognised as important. There are also detailed variations in the nature of the lipids in different foodstuffs; you may have encountered discussions about the importance of polyunsaturated fatty acids, especially omega-3 fatty acids, a component of lipids found particularly in oily fish and some seeds.

Without more detail, it is difficult to comment on the adequacy of the 1920s Chinese diet, but it is likely that it was, at best, barely adequate, and probably limited both the growth and activity of those eating it. This would also have been true for poorer areas of Europe and the USA at that time. Today, when the UK population consider themselves to be well fed, it is suggested that they eat too much meat, and not enough fruit and seed products, for good health. You may like to consider whether the person detailed in SAQ 2.1 is taking heed of such advice!

SAQ 2.1   Basic diet analysis

Today, I consumed the following foods:

Breakfast

Porridge and a banana

Lunch

Bacon and tomato sandwich, pot of fruit yoghurt, piece of fruit cake

Evening meal

Helping of beef casserole with potatoes, turnip, carrot

Fruit pie with wholemeal crust.

(a) As a semi-retired adult, what is the recommended amount of food energy for me per day?

(b) Compare and contrast this diet with that outlined for rural Chinese in 1920.

(c) Identify the main sources of food energy and protein in this diet.

Summary of Section 2

In the mid twentieth century, Chinese diets were very different from those consumed in present-day Europe or America, comprising mainly plant materials with very small quantities of meat. However, it appears that they probably provided the bare essential nutrient needs of the population.

3 Chinese agriculture in the 1920s

A major problem for China has always been the relative shortage of cultivable land, and the variability of the land that was available. Mountains, deserts and other dry or cold lands that were unfit for cultivation (Figures 2.1 and 2.2) made up between 60 and 70 per cent of the total land surface, and the majority of the cropped land and population was concentrated in the plains between the mountains in the west and north and the sea to the east (Figure 2.5). In the plains, *alluvial* materials eroded from higher areas and deposited by wind and water gave good soils. In these fertile areas, food production was carried out with great labour intensity, using *terracing, irrigation* and *multiple cropping*, where more than one crop would be grown on the same land, either together or in sequence during a year. The wet rice landscape (Figure 2.6) is possibly the one most associated with China in the eyes of the rest of the world.

So how did it all work? The yield of a crop (the amount grown per unit area) depends on the amount of light energy that the crop can intercept and on the availability of water and plant nutrients. Crop plants need substantial quantities of water, three *macronutrients*, nitrogen (N) phosphorus (P) and potassium (K), and trace quantities of a range of *micronutrients*. If you are a gardener, you may be familiar with the NPK analysis that appears on packs of manufactured *fertiliser* used to supply additional nutrients. Where appropriate, additional irrigation water can be taken from rivers or lakes. The input of light energy from the Sun cannot be changed, but weeds growing with the crop can intercept light before it reaches the crop. Attacks by pests and diseases can either reduce the area of leaf, and hence light interception, or reduce the efficiency with which the leaves use the light. Weeds also compete with the crop for water and nutrients from the soil, so it is important to control or remove them.

Agroecosystems, that is, ecosystems that are designed to produce specific products, need to be carefully managed. You may recall from Block 4 the ways in which the Amerindian peoples used fire to modify the vegetation and to release plant nutrients for their crops. The wet system of rice growing, where the land is flooded for at least part of the year, (Figure 2.6) was a particularly effective means of controlling weeds and pests that could not survive under water, although it did little to check plant disease spread. Modern European or American agriculture uses industrially produced fertilisers to supply additional nutrients, pesticides to control undesired organisms and machinery for almost all cropping operations. In contrast, agroecosystems in 1920s China relied almost entirely on animal or human labour and locally sourced materials.

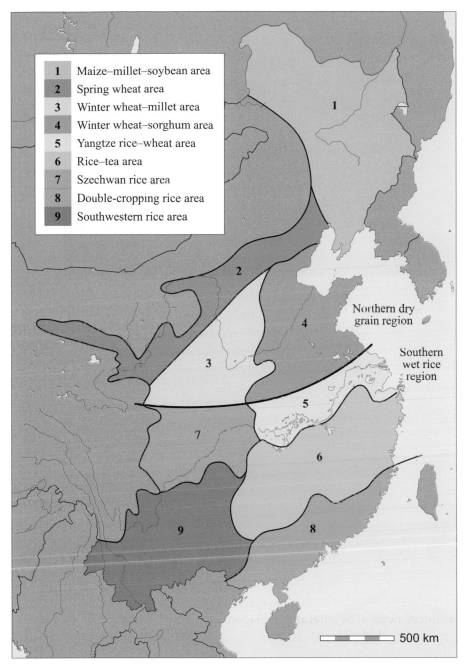

1 Maize–millet–soybean area
2 Spring wheat area
3 Winter wheat–millet area
4 Winter wheat–sorghum area
5 Yangtze rice–wheat area
6 Rice–tea area
7 Szechwan rice area
8 Double-cropping rice area
9 Southwestern rice area

Northern dry grain region

Southern wet rice region

500 km

Figure 2.5 Major cropping regions of China in the 1920s

Importantly, the Chinese systems were designed and managed to minimise loss of plant nutrients. The close proximity of rural Chinese consumers to the land from which the food was derived meant that human excrement ('night soil') and other decomposable domestic wastes could be returned direct to the soil. These wastes contain reasonable amounts of all three macronutrients, although these can be easily lost through *leaching* by rain.

Figure 2.6 Landscape of eastern China

Nitrogen can also be lost as ammonia gas from decomposing wet organic matter. Figure 2.7 shows a model of a combined pigsty and privy, in which the wastes from humans and pigs would be collected, and subsequently composted in a manure house. The eleventh century writer Chen Fu, quoted in Joseph Needham's 1984 series on *Science and Civilisation in China*, describes the system in detail:

> Beside every farmer's dwelling there should be a manure house (*fen wu*) with low eaves and posts to keep out the wind and rain; besides, if exposed to the sky the manure will lose its fertility. Inside the house a deep pit is dug, lined with bricks to prevent seepage. Into it go all sweepings, ashes, husks and chaff from winnowing, chopped straw and fallen leaves, all of which are accumulated in the pit burned and enriched with liquid manure (*fen chih*) and kept for as long as possible [before use].

(Needham, 1984)

Figure 2.7 Model of a combined pigsty and privy from the Han dynasty (200BC–AD200)

Even the most enthusiastic home composter in twenty-first century UK is unlikely to go to such lengths! In addition to locally produced wastes, human waste from the cities was transported out to the farmland (Figure 2.8). The composting process mentioned above should result in the mixture of materials heating up to a temperature sufficient to kill many pathogens, so the system was not as dangerous to human health as we might now assume. In addition, some wastes were actually cooked, to improve the availability of nutrients and, incidentally, to sterilise them.

(a)

(b)

Figure 2.8 (a) Collection of city night soil for transport to rural areas as fertiliser; (b) spreading collected night soil

Not all the nutrients could be retained within the agroecosystem. One loss was the use of crop residues as domestic fuel for cooking and heating. The stems of maize and kaoliang (millet) were allowed to dry in the field, and then either used locally as fuel or bundled up and sold to nearby urban areas. The ash from burning these might be returned to the soil, and would still contain most of the phosphorus and potassium of the original material, but the relatively small amount of nitrogen present in the stems would be lost as gaseous nitrogen oxides. In Block 4 you encountered the carbon cycle, whereby carbon atoms move between different reservoirs. Similar cycles occur for the major plant nutrients. For nitrogen, the cycle is basically similar to that of carbon, except that plants cannot take up nitrogen directly from the air, but only as soluble nitrogen-containing compounds from the soil. These soluble compounds are formed from proteins in animal metabolism, then excreted as urine. They are also formed by the decomposition of dead plant and animal material in the soil. Beans, such as soya (Figure 2.3), were important to the agroecosystem because they are *legumes* which, through the action of *symbiotic bacteria* living in nodules on their roots, are able to convert nitrogen gas from the air into a soluble form that can be utilised as a major nutrient by the host plant. This process is called *nitrogen fixation*, and in wet rice cultivation, blue-green algae present in the water can also carry this out. There is no direct transfer of nitrogen back to the atmosphere from plants and animals comparable to the loss of carbon dioxide in respiration, but nitrogen does return to the atmosphere through decomposition processes involving *bacteria* and other organisms in the soil.

Activity 2.2   Nutrient cycles in Chinese agroecosystems

The main reservoirs of nitrogen for a small rural holding in the rice growing area of 1920s China were the atmosphere, soil, humans, plants (both legumes and non-legumes), dead organic matter and domestic animals. Using the information provided here and in Block 4, draw a flow diagram to show how nitrogen as a plant nutrient might be cycled round these reservoirs.

Discussion
Figure 2.9 shows the basic flows between these reservoirs. It does not show some potential losses from the system, in the small amounts of crop materials that were sold off the holding and losses in water that flows through or over the soil and out of the holding.

The role of livestock in the 1920s Chinese food chain is interesting. The heavier cultivation work, and most rural transport, depended on animals such as water buffalo, well suited to wet rice cultivation, and oxen and donkeys for transport. So there were quite a lot of animals about, yet only tiny quantities of meat were eaten. In the typical 1920s Chinese diet, meats were largely pork, chicken and fish or shellfish with some mutton, but also a number of less familiar items, including dog. Beef did not feature in any significant form, nor did milk and cheese, despite the presence of water buffalo and oxen that could be milked, or eaten at the end of their working lives. For many rural Chinese, eating buffalo and oxen was culturally unacceptable and it was believed that it would cause poor harvests. Yet there is a Chinese saying that they will eat anything with legs except the table! The animals that were kept specifically for food were all individually small, so a family might be able to keep a single pig or a few chickens in a limited space. Cattle come in bigger individual units, and were probably beyond the economic or land area limits of a single family except as draft animals. Incidentally, many Chinese people do not retain the ability to absorb *lactose*, the form of sugar found in cows' milk, into adulthood, unlike northern Europeans.

Biologically, pigs and chickens are what are called *monogastric* (single-stomached) animals, and they need a diet basically similar to our own. In practice, pigs, ducks, geese and chickens (Figure 2.10) can forage for feed,

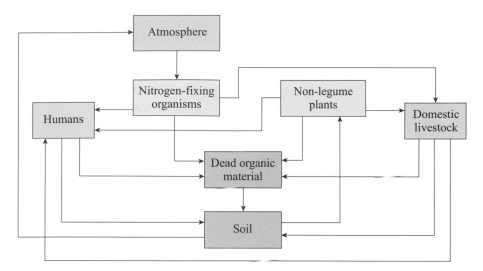

Figure 2.9 Flow diagram of the nitrogen cycle for Chinese peasant farm in the 1920s

Figure 2.10 Geese feeding on the edge of a flooded rice field

eating soil organisms and other small items that would be impossible or grossly time consuming for people to collect and eat. Pigs and chickens can also consume food rejected by humans.

Sheep, cattle and goats are *ruminants*, with a specially adapted series of 'stomachs' occupied by bacteria and *protozoa* that enable them to survive on a diet of grass and other materials consisting primarily of *cellulose*, which cannot be digested by humans. This means that ruminants can graze on areas unsuitable for crop production, and produce useable food as meat or milk. Fish, such as carp (Figure 2.11), can be purely plant eaters (*herbivores*) although they do not possess the special digestive mechanisms of ruminants. They live on plants growing in the water or undigested plant material in human and animal faeces deposited into the water. Other fish species are *carnivores*, eating other animals including smaller fish or other smaller water-dwelling organisms. Both herbivorous and carnivorous fish can therefore concentrate the soup of materials and tiny organisms in a pond or stream into a neat package to be eaten by a human. Depositing human and animal wastes into the water stimulates plant growth, to the benefit of the fish as well as ensuring effective nutrient cycling. The fish–rice system is a fascinating agroecosystem, with the rice taking up soluble nutrients from the water and providing shade to stabilise water temperature for the fish. Waste products from the fish provided soluble nutrients for the rice, and the fish controlled weeds and disturbed the underlying soil, which also helped plant growth.

Figure 2.11 Grass carp

There were therefore good biological reasons for consumption of products from those animals that could utilise resources otherwise unavailable to humans. They provided a relatively small but important contribution to diet in the areas of wet rice cultivation. In the uncultivable lands of north and west China (Figure 2.2), livestock were a major source of food for the nomadic peoples of those areas (Figure 2.12). Their flocks of sheep, cattle and goats were able to graze on the sparse vegetation, providing meat and milk that could be fermented to remove the lactose and to form a relatively stable cheese that could be stored for use when necessary.

(a)   (b)

Figure 2.12 (a) Nomadic herders in north-western China; (b) shepherd

SAQ 2.2   Agriculture

What similarities and differences can you see between Chinese rice-based agriculture in the 1920s and the systems of food production in Amazonia described in Block 4? You should think in particular about nutrient cycles and the effect of food production on the local ecology.

Summary of Section 3

Chinese agriculture in the mid twentieth century was designed to supply the mainly plant-based diet for the rural population, using large amounts of labour, careful landscaping and use of water, multiple cropping and very tight nutrient cycling. Livestock were used primarily to provide draft power and as scavengers to maintain the tight nutrient cycles.

4 An assessment of twentieth century Chinese food production

The area of land cultivated for food production in China increased from 50 million hectares in 1685 to 83 million hectares in 1893 and 120 million hectares in 1936 (Croll, 1983) through the use of terracing, irrigation and other developments, a much greater rate of increase than occurred in Europe over the same period. Grain production is estimated to have risen from about 20 million tonnes in 1400 to 75 million tonnes in 1770 and 130 million tonnes by 1940, to match a population that increased from about 200 million in 1750 to 430 million in 1913. Although some of the systems of food production described may look antiquated to modern eyes, they were actually a very sophisticated adaptation to circumstances. The iron mouldboard plough (Figure 2.13), which finally became a mainstay of European agriculture in the eighteenth and nineteenth centuries, was in common use for dry-land cultivation in China in the seventh century, and may have first been developed eight or nine centuries earlier. Indeed, Bray (writing in Needham, 1984) and others suggest that many other developments in European agriculture can be traced back to China. The idea of cultivating crops in rows so that it was possible to weed between them is supposed to have been invented in China at least 2100 years BP, and a form of seed drill for setting the seed in rows 1800 years BP. These techniques are usually claimed to have been invented in England in the eighteenth century.

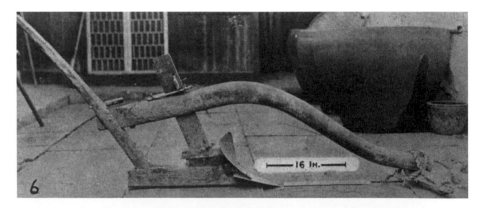

Figure 2.13 Chinese mouldboard plough. This is a mid twentieth century example, but is little changed from forms developed two thousand years earlier

New, early-maturing strains of rice that allowed two crops to be grown each year were being selected as early as the fifteenth century. Maize and potatoes were introduced from the Americas in the sixteenth century. According to one investigator (Vavilov, 1992) 136 species of plants were first domesticated in China, one of the largest numbers anywhere in the world.

The south-eastern part of China is now recognised as one of the biodiversity hotspots of the world. These hotspots are areas with an unusually high diversity of species. The giant panda (Figure 2.14) is just one iconic example from this area.

Figure 2.14 Giant panda, an iconic species of conservation interest

An assessment of the environmental impact of the Chinese food system in this period raises some interesting points. The wide range of plant and animal species that was used for human food production in itself represented a high biodiversity in the cropped areas. The landscapes and habitats present were closely managed but highly diverse, providing a wide variety of habitats for the survival of different species. The close association between the human population and the land on which they lived meant that the value of different species was widely recognised, implicitly if not explicitly, and these were generally exploited in such a way as not to deplete the living resource. Conservation was thus an integral part of the culture, although this idealised picture may have been associated with borderline undernutrition even at the best of times. In times of hardship through drought, floods or other stresses, we can imagine that this apparent care for long-term sustainability may have had to be subservient to short-term human survival.

Summary of Section 4

Mid-twentieth century Chinese agriculture appeared to provide adequate nutrition for the population, with minimal environmental impact, although the cultivated landscape was heavily modified and controlled.

You should now be able to comment on the environmental impact of Chinese agricultural practice in the early twentieth century.

5 The second half of the twentieth century

While the system of food production described so far had broadly been successful in feeding the population, it was critically dependent on weather, soil conditions and the skills of the peasant farmers. Floods in the fertile river valleys and droughts in the northern provinces occurred frequently, causing serious local famines even in the twentieth century. A second problem was that there was little opportunity for rural families to earn money with which to purchase better seeds or strains of livestock, additional nutrients, mechanical pumps for irrigation, or soil-engaging machinery such as tractor-drawn cultivators that were becoming common in Europe and the USA by the mid twentieth century. Socially, there were also potentially damaging divisions between the successful (or lucky) landholders who, with access to more or better land, had a surplus of crops or livestock to sell, and those who had to live from hand to mouth. One anthropologist distinguished four classes within a northern village on the basis of diet. The poorest families relied on sweet potato, the slightly richer could afford millet as well. Above them, millet and wheat were possible, and the richest ate mainly wheat, as well as meat.

This class distinction, among other factors, contributed to the success of the Communist party under Mao ZheDong. For some decades, the reforms he introduced increased China's food production and ensured its fairer distribution. Table 2.6 shows the changes in population, gross grain output and amount available per capita from 1949, when the Communists took unchallenged power, to 1974.

Table 2.6 Chinese grain production and availability 1949–1974

	1949	1952	1957	1965	1974
Population (millions)	538	570	640	726	894
Grain production (/tonnes $\times 10^9$)	111	161	191	204	275
Available grain per person per annum (kg)	206	282	298	281	308

Derived from Croll, 1983, Table 5

To examine the effect of these changes on the supply of food energy from grain, we need to make assumptions about its food energy content. The data for grain in Table 2.6 refers to unprocessed grain, which contains very little water, so it would be misleading to use the data in Table 2.5, which refers to processed forms such as boiled rice, bread or noodles. These have a higher water content, and water does not provide any food energy. The nearest item to unprocessed grain in Table 2.5 is probably wholemeal flour, which has an energy value of 1351 kJ per 100 g. So for unprocessed grain an estimate of 1200 kJ per 100 g or 12 MJ per kg (1200 kJ = 1.2 MJ, 100 g = 0.1 kg) is probably reasonable.

Activity 2.3   Food energy supplies

Using these assumptions about the food energy value of grain, estimate the food energy available per person per day in 1949 and 1974.

Discussion

In 1949, there was 206 kg of grain available per person per year, equivalent to 206/365 = 0.56 kg per person per day. This would supply 0.56 × 12 = 6.8 MJ of food energy per day. Compared with the current data for Europeans given in Table 2.4, this represents a very low figure although, as noted earlier, possibly just about adequate. By 1974, there was (308/365) × 12 = 10.1MJ, which sounds much more reasonable. It has been estimated that in 1974, the grain supply represented between 80 and 110 per cent of basic nutritional requirement.

The way in which Mao ZheDong achieved this steadily rising supply of grain has been a matter of controversy. From 1920 until the communists came to power in the 1940s, decisions about food production were taken by the peasants, who operated their holdings independently. Their first requirement was to feed themselves, selling any surplus to purchase other items. Once in power, Mao instituted a system of **production teams** and brigades that managed all the cultivable land on a communal basis. In return for work for the **brigades**, peasants were supplied with grain and other food material from the communal store; those unable to work were also fed by the brigade as a social duty. To varying degrees, the peasants were also allowed to work small private plots (Figure 2.15), mainly to produce vegetables or other more tasty components of traditional foods (cai). You can see an echo of this in the plots cultivated by Jackie's parents and described on The Migration Story audio.

Figure 2.15 Private plot growing vegetables

The advantages of the brigade system were the advantages of scale – larger machinery could be used where appropriate, management did not depend on the vagaries of skill levels of individual peasant operators and new technologies could be rapidly introduced nationally. The state-controlled procurement of grain meant that all the population, rural or urban, were assured of a basic supply of food. Mao's experience as a guerrilla fighter had convinced him of the importance of grain supplies.

> Red rice, pumpkin soup, Dig wild vegetables as our food,
>
> Commissioner Mao is with us, Every meal will be tasty.

This couplet from the song 'Commissioner Mao Is with Us' originated in the Jinggangshan Revolutionary Base in east China's Jiangxi province, where Mao Zedong, then an alternate member of the Political Bureau of the Communist Party of China (CPC) Central Committee, successfully led the Autumn Harvest Uprising in the Hunan–Jiangxi Border Region in 1927.

As one of the most popular 'revolutionary songs' still sung today, it reflects the hardships of the CPC-led Red Army in fighting the Kuomintang troops. Red rice and pumpkin soup are local specialities in the Jinggang Mountains and a part of the visitor experience today.

The red rice, a coarse staple, was eaten without much seasoning in 1927, and the pumpkin soup was commonly described as 'not revolutionary enough' as hunger usually returned very soon after its consumption.

Without a regular supply chain, the Red Army, later renamed the People's Liberation Army, drove back the invading Japanese army and defeated the Kuomintang with its simple 'xiaomi jia buqiang' or 'millet and rifle' approach.

(Quoted in Li and Cheng, 2007)

Activity 2.4   The role of grain as a foodstuff

From the data in Table 2.5, and from your general knowledge, why would grains be particularly valuable as food to a guerrilla group?

Discussion

A highly mobile guerrilla group would need to be able to carry foodstuffs that would not easily spoil, and would supply a reasonable balance of energy and protein for a given weight. From Table 2.5, bread and flour derived from grain, and some of the animal products, provide a good balance of these two essentials, but from your daily experience, you are probably aware that meat does not keep well outside a refrigerator. Dry grains are light to carry for a given energy supply and will keep for a long period if they are kept dry. Even when converted into flour, they are still reasonably stable. However, there are some vitamins and other nutrients that are not available from grains, so a purely grain diet needs to be supplemented with some vegetables and fruit. You may like to speculate where and how guerrillas might obtain these.

Mao's fixation on grain production was based on sound reasoning for his original circumstances, but he was not an agricultural specialist, and some of his centrally imposed demands for grain production by the brigades ignored the actual cropping potential of their land. In some areas, the production norm for grain was totally unrealistic, and to achieve these the brigades cut down trees and attempted to cultivate grassland and scrubland that were essential to keeping the soil in place.

> Move hills, Fill Gullies and create Plains. Destroy Forests. Open Wastelands.

> *(Slogans from the Mao era)*

Some, at least, of the problems with China's soil are inherent, but Mao ZheDong's actions certainly did not help. The story of Zhang Liubao, an enthusiastic disciple, is probably typical.

> Zhang Liubao returned […] to his home village of Zuitou full of inspiration. Zuitou was so impoverished […] that people ate just one or two good meals a year. Following Zhang's instructions, villagers fanned out, cutting the scrubby trees on the hillsides, slicing the slopes into earthen terraces, and planting millet on every newly created flat surface. […] Ultimately, Zhang said, they increased Zuitou's farmland by 'about a fifth' – a lot in a poor place.

> Alas, the actual effect was to create a vicious circle […]. Zuitou's terrace walls made of nothing but packed silt continually fell apart, hence Zhang's need to constantly shore up collapsing terraces. Even when the terraces didn't erode, rains sluiced away the nutrients and organic matter in the soil. After the initial rise, harvests started dropping. To maintain yields, farmers cleared and terraced new land, which washed away in turn.

> *(Mann, 2008)*

Once the state norms for production had been satisfied, there was no incentive for peasants to produce any additional grain and most preferred where possible to devote any spare time to their private plots. As noted in Part 1, this work was not valued commercially, so did not feature in data such as GDP, a matter of national pride and on which government decisions were often based. In 1959–61, Mao attempted what was known as the Great Leap Forward, which involved increasing steel production to enable large scale and rapid industrialisation so that China could '… [overtake] Great Britain in industrial production within 15 years'. According to current interpretations, this required brigades to mine and smelt iron as well as producing food (Figure 2.16). Land was stripped to mine iron ore, work on private plots was outlawed and grain production slumped, possibly by as much as 30%. Depending on whose account is to be believed, up to 30 million people starved to death during this period and little useful steel was actually produced. The pollution from the dispersed industries was horrific, and further large areas of forest were felled to provide charcoal for the smelting process, exposing the soil to risks of *erosion* by rain.

Figure 2.16 Village-scale iron smelting

The policies of the Great Leap Forward were quietly rescinded, and with the accession of a more flexible leadership in 1978 food production once more began to develop to keep pace with the expanding population. The new regime encouraged increasing mechanisation to improve the timeliness of cultivation operations, use of industrially produced fertilisers (see below), *pesticides* to control weeds and pests and further use of improved crop varieties. Thus the agroecosystem changed from being one that was more or less self contained to one that depended on a number of external inputs. Despite the setbacks of the Great Leap Forward, Chinese industrial production began to increase rapidly after 1978, encouraging and requiring the migration to the cities described in Part 1. This urbanisation leads to different relations between the population and the food supply, described in Section 6.

SAQ 2.3   Agricultural development in China

Outline the strengths and weaknesses of Chinese agricultural policy during the period 1947 to 1980. What were the environmental consequences of these policies?

Summary of Section 5

In the latter half of the twentieth century, China itself and its methods of food production underwent a series of upheavals. Although some more 'modern' agricultural techniques were introduced, and crop yields were increased, the political turmoil of the period also resulted in serious mistakes being made, with severe consequences for the land and for those living in rural areas.

Food and agriculture in modern China

6

China in the early years of the twenty-first century is very different from what has been described in Sections 2–5. The major change has been the rapid urbanisation, with many more people living in cities. This has enabled enormous growth in industrial production, but has interesting consequences for food production.

6.1   Feeding the growing cities

Feeding cities, as opposed to feeding a peasant family growing its own food, introduces additional complications to the food chain 'from field to fork'. Foodstuffs have to be collected from the rural areas, stored and transported to urban areas. The traditional dominance of seeds and seed products in the Chinese diet initially made it relatively easy to provide basic foodstuffs for the growing cities. Provided they are kept relatively dry and free from pests, grains will degrade relatively slowly, since *spoilage organisms* such as bacteria and fungi require water to grow. Foodstuffs with a higher water content, such as root vegetables and fruits, are more difficult to store, since spoilage organisms can grow rapidly in the wetter tissues. Natural processes of degradation that occur as the materials age are also more rapid in wetter materials. To prevent deterioration in these products they either have to be stored at low temperature or *processed* in some way, often by heating or creating some form of barrier, to destroy or prevent access by the spoilage organisms.

Activity 2.5   Food processing

Suggest some examples of food processing to enhance the keeping qualities of foodstuffs with which you are familiar. What additional environmental costs might be incurred by each of these processes?

Discussion
Probably the most familiar storage process in Europe now is the refrigerator or deep freeze, where foodstuffs can be stored for periods of days or months by keeping them at a low enough temperature to retard spoilage processes. The environmental (and financial) cost of refrigeration comes from the need for a continuous supply of electricity to maintain the low temperature. The manufacture of refrigeration machinery also requires energy and resources and, until recently, the escape of the gases used for cooling was a major threat to the ozone layer in the atmosphere.

Another example is the steel or aluminium can (Figure 2.17) or glass bottle used for fruits, some vegetables and meat products. While the container itself acts as a barrier to spoilage organisms, the food material has to be **heat-treated** at some point to destroy spoilage organisms that are already present and to deactivate the **enzymes** in the foodstuffs that would otherwise cause deterioration. The heat treatment requires energy and there are both resource and energy costs involved in making the container. Unless they are reused or recycled, disposing of the containers can result in pollution, as will be outlined in Bottled Water – Who Needs It? in Part 3.

Drying fruits and meats allows them to be stored for some months. Other processes include pickling and salting. Pickling involves adding or producing an acid in the food, which stops most spoilage organisms growing, as does the presence of high salt concentrations. In Europe, we probably think of these processes as methods for changing flavour (pickled onions, salt beef, etc.) but they were originally used for preservation. Salted and pickled vegetables were used in rural Chinese diets to even out seasonal fluctuations in supply. All these processes incur costs, and may affect our environment. Drying, unless it relies on the Sun, requires fuel. Pickling and salting do not need much energy, but the flavour changes they cause may be unpopular and there is some evidence that eating both pickled foods and heavily salted meats over a long period of time may cause health problems.

Figure 2.17 Canning factory

6.2   Chinese agriculture in the twenty-first century

The increasing, and increasingly urban, population meant that Chinese agriculture also had to change, perhaps even more spectacularly, and certainly more successfully, than it had under Mao ZheDong. While the tight nutrient cycles of the 1920s were effective in maintaining yields, these yields were limited by the total nutrient supply to the crops. A major factor in the country's continued ability to feed its growing population has been the increasing use of synthesised fertilisers to supply the major plant nutrients N, P and K, as shown in Table 2.7 and Figure 2.18.

Table 2.7 Synthetic fertiliser consumption* in China from 1957 to 1999			
Year	N fertiliser	P fertiliser	K fertiliser
1957	320	53	0
1965	1,333	111	4
1975	3,407	1,659	146
1980	9,424	2,897	373
1990	17,409	6,679	1,821
1999	24,450	12,252	4,543

*All units are 10^3 tonnes

Source: Gao et al., 2006

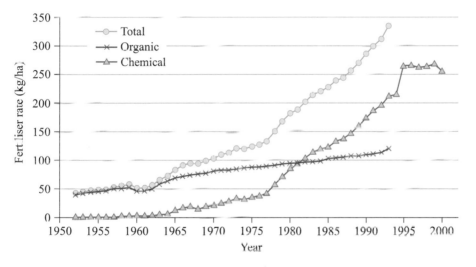

Figure 2.18 Application rates of organic and synthetic fertilisers in China since the 1950s. *Source: Heilig (1999)*

Activity 2.6   Fertiliser use in China

Summarise briefly the general trends shown in Figure 2.18.

Discussion

The graph suggests that synthetic fertiliser use per hectare began to increase in about 1965, possibly as a reaction to the disaster of the Great Leap Forward, and use increased rapidly from about 1978 onwards, following the reforms introduced by the changed regime. The application of organic manures from livestock, human excreta, composted plant materials and silts from irrigation channels increased somewhat in the mid 1960s, but more slowly thereafter. A particularly striking feature is the levelling off of synthetic fertiliser use per hectare in 1995.

The plateau in fertiliser use per hectare from 1995 may be an illustration of an important general principle, that of *diminishing returns*. The additional benefit obtained from each successive addition of some input to a process often decreases as more and more input is used. So the additional crop yield for each successive kilogram of fertiliser applied decreases until there comes a point where there is no further increase, no matter how much more is applied. This is an example of *Liebig's law of the minimum*, which states that the rate of any process, such as the growth of a plant, is limited by whatever factor is in shortest relative supply, the *limiting factor*, at that time. Increasing the amount of nitrogen available to a crop will have no effect if growth is limited by the availability of some other nutrient, water or light. This has important economic implications. If spending an extra $1 on fertiliser results in an increase in grain harvested that is worth $1.2, then it is worthwhile spending that money on extra fertiliser, since it gives an extra *marginal return* of $0.2. But as more is applied, and the response decreases, the extra dollar's worth of fertiliser may only produce an increased yield worth $1.01, so the marginal return is only $0.01. If the increased yield from an extra $1 spent on fertiliser is only worth $0.9, then the marginal return is negative and it is clearly silly to apply the extra. In theory, an *economically rational* operator would apply just enough fertiliser for the cost of the last extra kilogram applied and the value of the additional crop produced to be equal, known as the point of *zero marginal return*. This sort of analysis can be applied to all sorts of economic activities.

SAQ 2.4   Economics of fertiliser use

If, in 1995, Chinese farmers were operating in an economically rational manner, explain what Figure 2.18 suggests about the relationship between fertiliser price, grain price and the response of crops to additional fertiliser application.

Production of fertiliser needs an industrial infrastructure and this has other costs on top of the economic ones. Fertilisers containing phosphorus and potassium have to be mined and extracted from rocks rich in these elements and this requires the use of energy, probably from fossil fuels. Each kilogram of phosphorus or potassium in fertiliser currently requires 8.6 or 6.4 MJ of support energy respectively. Nitrogen-containing fertilisers are synthesised from the nitrogen in the air, needing about 65 MJ to produce 1 kg of nitrogen as fertiliser. Synthesis of pesticides is less energy intensive per unit used, but still represents an additional input to the food production system. Tractors and other machinery require energy to run them, but also require energy and materials for their manufacture. As noted earlier, China has a limited area of cultivable land, and much of this requires special small (mainly Japanese) machinery shown in Figure 2.19. Unlike a water buffalo, this machinery does not reproduce itself, so needs more industrial infrastructure.

Figure 2.19 A modern harvesting scene in China. Note the small size of the machinery used compared with the type of machinery you might see in Europe or the USA

The other environmental cost of increased fertiliser use is pollution. High levels of nitrogen fertiliser use can give rise to losses of nitrous oxide, another greenhouse gas, from the soil. Unless fertiliser is applied carefully, so that it is all taken up by the crop, any surplus can be leached into water courses and lakes or into the groundwater supplying wells. In open water, the increased supply of plant nutrients leads to rapid growth of algae and water plants, the process of *eutrophication*. If this plant material was utilised, as in the fish–rice system, this would be no problem, but a sudden flush of growth may be more than the fish can consume. The excess plant growth dies off and begins to decompose, a process that uses up the oxygen that is dissolved in the water. If this is not replaced by oxygen diffusing in from the air, then the oxygen in the water can fall to such low levels that fish and other aquatic life is killed off. The debris poses a further demand on the oxygen supply. Excess nutrients in groundwater may, in association with other forms of pollution, cause direct damage to human health. These off-farm effects had become a serious problem in Europe and the USA, and China is following the same path.

China's historic success in feeding its population has relied on the careful use of the available land and water through irrigation, terracing and the ability to cultivate tiny individual areas. There was tight nutrient cycling and control of diseases and pests used hand weeding or flooding of rice paddies. In contrast, conventional modern agriculture, in China as elsewhere (Figure 2.18), relies much more on machinery, synthesised fertilisers and pesticides applied to highly developed *cultivars* of the different crops selected usually for their ability to respond to high plant nutrient levels.

Between 1978 and 2004, fossil energy consumption for arable production in China almost tripled, from 1446 petajoules (PJ) (1 PJ = 10^{15} J) to 4092 PJ. China had the highest use of fertiliser per hectare of arable land in the world in 2008 and the world's largest total use of fertilisers and pesticides (Shuyan Cao et al., 2008). However, Shuyan Cao et al. (2008) suggest that the fertiliser used was often of inappropriate composition relative to the nutrient needs of the crops. The nutrient in shortest relative supply would restrict crop growth (Liebig's law again) and any surplus of other nutrients could be leached out, leading to eutrophication problems. Other research suggests that the potential yield of crops in China could also be increased by the use of improved varieties, irrigation or better pest and disease control, as shown in Table 2.8.

Table 2.8 Estimated potential and actual 1994 yield of crops in China*

	Wheat	Maize	Rice	Soya bean
Potential yield	5.4	9.9	8.1	3.6
Actual yield	2.7	3.8	5.1	1.8

*All units are tonnes per hectare

Source: Mingkui Cao et al., 1995

Table 2.8 suggests that it might be possible to about double the 1994 yields of wheat and soya beans and to gain even more for maize. (For comparison, in 2008, average yields of wheat in the UK were around 9 tonnes per hectare.) Rice yields in China in 1994 were already quite a high proportion of the estimated potential, a reflection of China's long history of rice cultivation.

Chinese agriculture has been skilful in its use of water, a limiting factor over much of the intensively cultivated eastern half of the country. However, water is also needed for industry and used, even if not needed, for the disposal of industrial wastes, as you will see in Part 3. As a result, a major limitation on Chinese food production may be competition for limited resources of water and contamination of supplies. This is illustrated in an account by Rob Gifford in the magazine *Prospect* in July 2008.

Zhao takes me through the back streets [of Baiyin, in north-eastern China] where factories cluster and multiply like cancer cells. Heavy metals of all sorts are being purified and refined, the waste being spat back into the local water supply. From smelters and factories comes a dark, fetid overflow which runs directly into the Yellow River [...]

At the tiny village of Tie ZhuQuan, about 60 miles from the river, Zhan Guangjing flips a switch and pumps his harvest of rainwater from a nearby pond on to his fields. His is one of the few ponds in the village that still holds water. [...]

I sit down with Zhang, a wiry 60 year old farmer and his neighbours in a courtyard. The villagers have complaints – the bumpy unpaved road, the cost of petrol and fertiliser – but on one problem they all agree. 'Water,' says Shao Zhong, who has spent all his 67 years here. 'We have always lacked water. And we lack money to help us do anything about it!'

Shao says an average household in the village uses about 3000 gallons of water a year – less than one tenth the consumption of a single American. For drinking water, they rely on rainwater gathered in cisterns and deep wells. For crops, there is only the rain. 'We still depend on heaven to survive,' he says.

(Gifford, 2008)

In addition to environmental costs, modern Chinese agriculture may also be creating problems for itself. The increasing mechanisation of Chinese agriculture has militated against the use of small, awkward areas, leading to these being abandoned. There have been several other changes in the total area that can be used for growing the main crops, shown in Table 2.9.

Table 2.9 Changes in land area used for major crops, 1988–1995[A]

Gains		Losses	
Reclamation of non-cultivated land	2200	Construction of factories and dwellings	–980
Drainage	121	Changed to horticulture	–1220
Re-use of abandoned land	349	Changed to fishponds	–226
Conversion from other use	413	Changed to grassland	–549
		Changed to forest land	–970
		Disasters	–856
Net change			–1722

*All units are thousands of hectares

Source: Heilig, 1999

Table 2.9 suggests that a significant area of land has been reclaimed for growing major crops. This presumably involved levelling, construction of new terraces, etc., although the cited reference does not explain this in detail. But overall, there has been a net decrease of some 1.7 million hectares in the area of arable land for the major crops. This is the equivalent of about one-twentieth of the total area of the UK or something over one-hundredth of the total cultivable area of China. Where the arable land has been converted to use for horticulture or fishponds, this may reflect changes in the nature of food demand from urban areas, as you will see later. Horticulture and fishponds still provide food, although in terms of crude food energy supply, not as much as would be obtained from staple crops. The other changes noted in Table 2.9 will have decreased food supply, and the net change in area does not tell us anything about the nature of the land, particularly soil conditions. Mechanisation of agriculture has possibly led to less care being taken of the soil, so that erosion and other forms of *land degradation* have increased. Forms of degradation include:

- water or wind erosion
- contamination
- waterlogging or, conversely, lowering of the water table through overextraction of groundwater
- loss of soil organic matter
- leaching out of soluble plant nutrients, also leading to groundwater pollution.

Some 40 per cent of the land in China has been estimated to suffer moderate to severe erosion. Water erosion affects mainly the east, south and south-west regions, while wind erosion is a problem in the north and north-west regions. Areas affected by soil erosion increased from 153 million hectares in the 1950s to 180 million hectares in the 1990s. Contamination by industrial wastes, by heavy metals from mining, and by acid air pollution from industries is reported to affect some 10 per cent of total farmed land, mostly near the more economically developed regions. Heavy metal contamination of grains has caused health problems for consumers. In 2007, the Chinese government set up an Integrated Ecosystem Management scheme to try to combat land degradation (Zhou Ke et al., 2008).

Activity 2.7   China and food supply

From the information above, does it seem likely that China can supply basic seeds-based foodstuffs for an increasing, and increasingly urban, population?

Discussion

Overall, I would say this might be feasible. Potential grain and pulse yields could be increased further, although the potential for rice may be more limited than for the other seeds. Modern Chinese agriculture is increasingly dependent on fossil fuel supplies, for machinery and for the production of fertilisers. Fertiliser use may be causing problems off-farm, and inappropriate use of machinery may damage the soil. Data on erosion and other forms of land degradation is worrying, especially given that China already has a very low area of cultivable land per capita. The data for the change in land available suggests that this could be a limit, but the actual changes represent only a very small proportion of the total, whereas the potential yield increases are a much larger proportion of current achievements. Several of the changes in Table 2.9 also relate to alternative food crop uses, particularly to horticulture, fishponds and to grassland. These could be reversed if necessary but, as I will discuss below, there are strong reasons for these changes, associated with the increasing standard of living in the urban areas.

Summary of Section 6

Many more of China's population now live in cities, and this leads to additional processes in food supply. Agriculture in China has changed even more dramatically over recent years. Inputs of externally produced fertilisers have increased, largely in response to economic factors, and there is increased use of fuel for use of machinery. This has allowed major changes in crop yields and in the use of land, but may have also resulted in damage to the soil. Food supply has so far kept pace with population increase.

7   Changing diets in China

The slightly optimistic prognosis presented here is predicated on Chinese citizens consuming their traditional, grain-based diet, albeit possibly not quite as extreme as the 1920s data given earlier. Historical evidence suggests that as people become richer, they eat less of the staples such as grains, but more, and a wider variety of, taste components such as meat and dairy produce. As noted earlier, China's economy had grown at around 10% annually between 1978 and 2007. Between 1981 and 2004 average per capita grain consumption is reported to have declined from 145 kg to 78 kg, while consumption of meat, eggs and fish/shellfish increased from 20, 5 and 7 kg respectively to 29, 10 and 12 kg (Dong and Fuller, 2007). There is also a shift to foods that are more convenient (Figure 2.20) than the crude grains. Recall from The Migration Story audio the sort of convenience food (beefburgers, pre-cooked ready meals, etc.) chosen by Jackie, in contrast to that eaten by her parents or by the poorer migrants.

Figure 2.20 The popularity of fast food in China

The environmental implications of these changes are interesting. Many of the convenience foods need to be stored under refrigeration, which is costly in energy terms. On the other hand, central cooking and preparation can actually use less energy per item than cooking in individual households. So in terms of fossil fuel need, these changes may balance out. Nutritionally, many convenience foods contain higher levels of salt and particularly fats than is nutritionally desirable. The fat and salt content is not essential to these foods, so producers could chose to reduce these. The question of packaging is more difficult. Convenience foods need to be packaged in plastics or similar materials to keep them from being contaminated. This improves hygiene and can reduce wastage of food, but packaging materials may be energy-expensive to produce and do not readily degrade when discarded. Food packaging is a major contributor to environmental pollution, as you shall see in Sections 9 and 10.

Changes in diet may have some major consequences. Recall from Section 2.1 that fats have a very high energy density of 38 MJ per kg. In addition, urban middle-class lifestyles are generally more sedentary, certainly in comparison with rural peasants. This could reduce their need for food energy, but appetite may not adjust accordingly. In 2008, Chinese children were approximately 60 mm taller than those of the same age in 1980, but there have also been dramatic increases in the rates of obesity among children in cities (see Figure 2.21). This suggests that their energy intake has equalled, and in many cases far exceeded, their energy demand over a continued period.

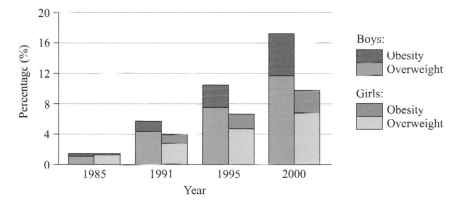

Figure 2.21 Percentage of schoolchildren overweight or with obesity in some large Chinese cities, 1985–2000

Summary of Section 7

Increasing affluence in the urban Chinese population has resulted in changes in diet, particularly in terms of meat consumption, and this may have resulted in some damaging effects on human health.

8   The meat consumption story

Meat consumption in China raises some important questions for sustainability. There is still some uncertainty over data about China's food consumption, as highlighted by Table 2.10, but whichever source is correct, it certainly appears that there has been a large increase in consumption of livestock products.

Table 2.10 Consumption of meat by Chinese citizens according to three different sources*				
Source	**1980**	**1985**	**1990**	**1995**
Food and Agriculture Organization of the United Nations	14.3	18.9	25.5	38.1
China Statistical Yearbook: urban consumers	n/a	22.0	25.2	23.7
China Statistical Yearbook: rural consumers	8.4	12.0	12.6	13.1

All units are kg per person per year

Source: Heilig, 1999

- Annual dairy sales in China are more than A$4 billion and are increasing by 30% per year.
- Milk and dairy product consumption is increasing by 10% annually.
- Raw milk production is expected to increase by about 25% annually.

Livestock is a key sector in China's agriculture and a top priority target for rapid development and modernization in China's current 5-year plan.

China is the world's largest livestock producer and consumer. China has more than 400 million cattle, sheep and goats, but pig and poultry meat and meat products are the most popular meat consumed in China. However, the consumption of beef and beef products, fresh milk and dairy products such as yogurt is increasing rapidly and is strongly encouraged by the Chinese government as a means of improving national health – especially for the elderly and the young through schemes such as the School Milk Program.

It is forecasted that China's consumption of meat and dairy products will continue to climb sharply due to a rising population, strong growth in per capita income, improvement in domestic meat and dairy production systems, greater access to meat and dairy products in the western and central parts of China due to better transportation and distribution systems, shifting consumption patterns and lower prices.

(*Agrifoodasia, n.d.*)

Some idea of the scale of Chinese livestock production is given by the following extract, written by an Australian journalist. Note that a *feedlot* is an American term for an enclosure where (usually) cattle are kept and fed on a diet of grain and other harvested materials rather than grazing for themselves. Feedstuffs might include *silage* made from grass or from cereals cut before they are fully ripe and allowed to ferment to prevent decay. The process is akin to pickling.

Whole lot of bull in Chinese cattle feedlot

Marius Cuming

Corporate agribusiness in China only comes in one size and that size is massive. The Fucheng feedlot near Beijing is a typical example. A fully vertically integrated operation, like many corporate businesses in China, the feedlot fattens and processes about 40,000 cattle a year. Taking a tour of the operation with Australian farmers is quite an experience in itself. Their eyes widen and a puzzled, if not amazed look washes over their faces when they see the production centre; the feedlot itself. As far as the eye can see there are cattle all tied to metal railings. Up to 15,000 beef cattle are individually tethered and fed in dozens of sheds with about 360 head in each. [...] The area is clean and tidy and the cattle, all bulls, appear calm and obviously accustomed to being handled. The animals are led out into the sunshine between sheds and tethered there for a few hours during the day and fed several times during the day as part of their 120-day feed ration. A high intensive operation in anybody's book but with over 4000 families employed and housed on the site, many Chinese hands make light work.

Cattle are sourced from markets across five provinces according to manager, Mr Zhang, who is more than happy to show the tourists around. Chinese workers at the feedlot smile as they go about their work, sweeping and cleaning the concrete. The feed to fuel this enormous beef engine is all grown in the surrounding districts. Corn and a sugar-cane like crop is cut into two to three inch pieces and stored like silage in massive pits on the site. Minerals are also added to the mix but no hormone growth promotants according to Mr Zhang, who insists the cattle are kept entire [i.e. uncastrated] to keep their growth rates up.

Cattle enter the lot at 350 kilograms and spend 120 days on the ration, gaining about two kilograms a day from the 25 kilograms fed to them before reaching their target weight of about 600 kilograms. It is at this point they walk no more than a few hundred metres to the abattoir; a state of the Chinese art facility. Mr Zhang said 180 cattle are processed every four hours at the works and 40,000 for the year. An amazing evolution from a company that started with seven cattle in 1986. Milk production has also become a part of the Fortune Ng Food Company that owns the operation. In the two dairy feedlots, 5000 cows produce 100,000 tonnes of milk per year.

These changes may have important implications for China's ability to feed itself and possibly for our biophysical environment. Increased meat consumption in China has involved increased use of grain as livestock feed. Maize consumption by livestock increased from 53 million tonnes in 1990 to

93 million tonnes in 2002, and soya bean meal from 1.03 million tonnes to 16.65 million tonnes over the same period (Yen et al., 2004). Since its accession to the World Trade Organization in 2001, China has become a major force in world commodity trade, including food and feed grains, and in 2008 was the world's largest importer of soya. Recall from Block 4 some of the possible effects that are seen in Amazonia from China's increased demand for soya.

At this point it is worth pausing to ask why Chinese people, along with the majority of humans, are so keen to consume animal products, especially given that some find this ethically unacceptable and there are suggestions that over-consumption of meat is bad for us. An overriding argument is that humans simply like meat, cheese and eggs. Another is that it is much easier to get protein and some other vital nutrients such as iron from animal products. Getting the same intake of these from vegetable products requires us to consume much larger quantities of (to me, often less palatable) vegetables. In almost all societies, eating meat has been regarded as a sign of high social status. Vegetarians may decry this, but it does seem very prevalent.

In 1920s China, livestock were used to convert otherwise unavailable materials into human food. Pigs and chickens scavenged and ate wastes, while ruminants such as sheep and goats relied mainly on land unsuitable for cropping, such as the semi-deserts of north-western China. In total, animals in the system increased the total food available as well as providing a valued component of *cai*. However, Chinese livestock are no longer just acting as scavengers or converters of inedible material but competing for maize and soya that is potentially suitable for human use. One kilogram of grain eaten directly by a human supplies about 12 MJ, more than a day's worth of food energy for an average adult. If that same kilogram of grain is fed to an animal then, depending on the animal, the food energy that we get when we eat it, drink its milk or eat its eggs is at best about 4 MJ, and at worst probably not more than 1 MJ.

So why in modern agriculture do we feed grain to livestock? To answer this, we need to consider some animal physiology and, because food production methods are largely dictated by the demands of an increasingly urban population, some economics. All livestock need food to grow and to produce meat, eggs or milk. The rate at which they grow depends on the amount of feed they consume and its quality. Every animal, including a human, has to eat some food, its *maintenance ration*, just to stay alive. Table 2.4 showed that a sedentary adult female human needs some 9.0 MJ of food energy to maintain a constant body weight. If that same woman is pregnant, she would need to consume 10.0 MJ to allow for the production of the foetus, or 11.3 MJ to survive and produce milk when lactating. For a child, additional energy on top of the basic weight-dependent maintenance ration is needed to produce new body tissue as it grows. For agricultural livestock, this extra feed needed for pregnancy, lactation or growth is called the *production* component of diet.

Let us now consider two young cattle, one of which is grazing on poor grassland, which restricts the amount of feed it can eat. Most of this is needed for maintenance, leaving little for production, so it can only grow slowly. The other animal also has access to unlimited cereal-based feed, so that it can eat as much as its appetite allows, enabling it to grow at the maximum rate governed by its genetic makeup. Figure 2.22(a) shows the amount of feed eaten by the fast-growing animal over its lifespan and its changing body weight. The amount of feed it needs each day for maintenance, the lower line, increases steadily with body weight, as does the total amount that it is capable of consuming, represented by the upper line. Mathematically, the total amount of feed it consumes over its lifespan is represented by the total area under the upper line. The maintenance component is represented by the shaded area, and the part of each day's consumption that is available for production by the unshaded part.

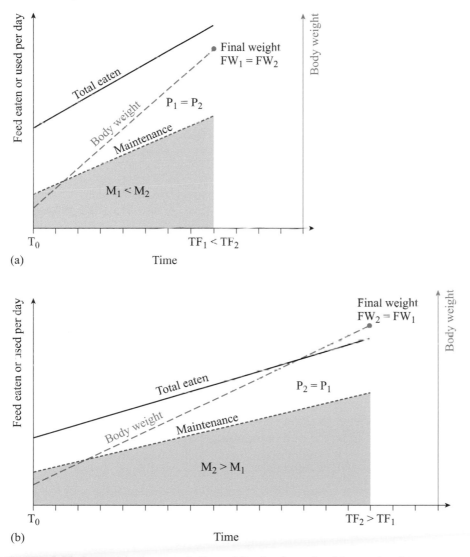

Figure 2.22 A graphical presentation of the feed needs of two animals consuming different amounts per day: (a) maximum intake; (b) restricted intake. The lower line represents feed eaten that is used for maintenance, the upper line is total feed consumed. The separate dashed green line represents the body weight of the animal

At a given body weight, each animal requires the same amount of feed for maintenance, and we want them to reach the same final weight. Physiologically, the total amount of feed needed for production of that body weight is the same, irrespective of the speed of growth. The intake of feed by the animal on the poor pasture (Figure 22(b)) is restricted, so it grows more slowly, and takes longer to reach the final desired weight. It thus has to eat its maintenance ration every day over a longer period. The feed used for production, represented by the unshaded area in the two graphs, is the same, but the lifetime maintenance requirement of the slower growing animal, the shaded area, is larger than that of the other. Overall, therefore, both animals produce the same final product as meat but the slower growing animal needs a larger total intake of feed, and is thus less efficient as a converter of its feed intake into final product.

Activity 2.8   Efficiency of feed conversion for other animal products

Consider whether a similar argument applies to the efficiency of conversion from feed into useful product for animals used to produce milk or eggs.

Discussion

The argument is exactly the same. The animals require the same maintenance ration at a given body weight irrespective of the rate at which they produce milk or eggs so, over a year, the animal with the higher feed intake and hence production rate produces more useful product, so tends to be the more efficient converter of feed to food.

Looking at this from an economic perspective, the choice between, for example, keeping cattle on poor pasture or feeding them cereals to allow them to grow faster comes down to relative costs and values. If cereals are cheap, then it may well make economic sense to feed these to livestock to enable them to grow faster or produce more milk/eggs, and to operate more efficiently in terms of useful production per unit of (cheap) feed consumed. Likewise, the land on which the animal lives has an economic value, represented by the rent or mortgage payments that have to be made to have access to it. It usually makes better sense to produce a rapidly growing animal in a short time by using some cereals than it does to produce one slow-growing one over a longer period, since the rent has to be paid no matter how fast the animal is growing. Hence we have the paradox that our economic demand for animal products leads to feedstuffs that could be used for humans being fed to livestock. This produces a more economically valuable product, but less total food energy per hectare, and raises the carbon footprint of the diet, as noted in Block 1. Some idea of the global importance of livestock can be gained from the fact that well over half of agricultural income in the USA comes from livestock.

SAQ 2.5   Dietary change and food provision

Summarise the implications for China of the documented changes in diet. Will these changes make it easier or more difficult to feed their population?

This discussion also raises an important point about system boundaries (Block 3). For the livestock rearer, the system of interest is the farm unit, and so the *measure of effectiveness* of that system is primarily the profit that can be obtained from that unit. In this context, grain feeding makes perfect sense, but in a finite world, a more appropriate measure of effectiveness may be the total amount of human food produced per hectare. The most effective production system in those terms would apparently use all land to grow crops. However, the crop production potential of different areas varies widely, from the grain lands of East Anglia in the UK to the semi-deserts of north-west China. If we take as our system of interest the entire land area of the world, then producing some livestock may still make considerable sense. Exploiting the semi-deserts for livestock may be better than ignoring them or attempting to cultivate them for crops, requiring irrigation or possibly damaging the soil. Grasslands such as the American prairies looked like perfect candidates for cultivation to grow food crops, but doing this caused the dustbowl of 1930s America (Figure 2.23 (a)) and may be leading to similar problems in China (Figure 2.23 (b)). Land kept under grass for erosion protection can still be cut or grazed, so livestock have a role there. Many of us value upland landscapes such as those of the English Lake District, and the appearance of these depends entirely on the presence of sheep grazing.

(a)

(b)

Figure 2.23 (a) Soil erosion from inappropriate cultivation: (a) in America – much of this land has now been returned to grassland or planted with trees; (b) in China

If the demand for ruminant meat exceeds what can be produced from areas that need to be kept under grass, then environmental costs increase. Deforestation for beef production in Amazonia was mentioned in Block 4 and the localised concentration of manure from the cattle feedlots described earlier can represent a source of pollution. Just getting rid of this manure can result in the nutrient cycle no longer being effectively closed, and the loss of nutrients to the overall agricultural system has to be made good with synthesised fertilisers. Fortunately, China has been a pioneer in the use of anaerobic digestion of manures, which produces methane for use as a fuel and a residue which retains the major plant nutrients and can be used as a fertiliser.

In the 1990s, there were about 5 million family-sized anaerobic digestion plants (Figure 2.24) operating in China (Marchaim, 1992) and that number is probably now nearer 8 million, supplying gas mainly for domestic cooking and heating.

Figure 2.24 Chinese fixed dome anaerobic digestion plant

Beef production has recently become an additional cause for concern relating to climate change. Ruminants' digestive processes depend on *anaerobic fermentation* within their complex stomachs (technically, their *rumen* and *reticulum*). These reactions, like those in landfilled wastes, produce methane, which they belch into the atmosphere. Depending on the exact diet that the animal is being fed, this can be as much as 700 litres per day, and it has been calculated that the total emissions of methane from ruminant livestock are 80 million tonnes per annum (United States Environmental Protection Agency, 2009). As methane is a powerful greenhouse gas, some 22 times more damaging than carbon dioxide, it is now being claimed that it is more important to reduce this source than to control carbon emissions from transport or other activities. While this may be special pleading, there is good reason to examine the fermentation process in the rumen to see if there are methods of reducing the production of methane. Economically, this could make excellent sense, since every gram of carbon lost as methane might otherwise contribute to nutrition of the animal. Wet-rice production is also a major source of methane, possibly emitting between 20 and 100 million tonnes per annum. Again, it is possible that changes to the management of the rice fields could reduce this without loss of rice yield.

Making decisions about meat consumption, as with all environmental decisions, therefore involves carefully considering system boundaries and measures of effectiveness. If we think that it is ethically acceptable to eat animal products, then a key question concerns the way in which those are produced. Should we go for the economically efficient use of grain for livestock, or should we only use grain for human consumption, with livestock as scavengers or grazers? If we value upland landscapes, do we have an alternative to livestock?

Summary of Section 8

This section has reviewed the implications of increasing meat consumption, and the economic and physiological reasons why this is usually associated with changes in the way that livestock are kept. The increased use of cereals to feed livestock competes with their direct use for human food, and Chinese demand for meat also has effects worldwide. However, the environmental case against the use of livestock is not clear cut.

9 How will China feed itself in the future?

This question may be more important than the simpler question of whether China could feed itself, considered in Activity 2.7, and relates to the wider question of how we feed a still-increasing world population without, if possible, damaging other aspects of our biophysical environment. History suggests that supplying the traditional Chinese diet for an increasing population had generally been successful over a long period, with the exception of some political aberrations such as the Great Leap Forward. But now, China's economic growth and urbanisation has encouraged and enabled major changes in diet associated with increasing affluence and has also increased industrial pollution. It is a basic tenet of development that consumers should expect to have increasing real spending power, and this is likely to result in similar dietary shifts in all societies as they become wealthier. This could reduce the overall availability of food compared with eating a diet closer to the traditional Chinese diet.

Activity 2.9   Food-related effects on the environment

Suggest one other food-related effect on our environment that you have previously read about and which may be affected by changes in the Chinese diet.

Discussion

The concept of food miles was introduced in Block 1. The shift from a restricted range of locally sourced, seasonally dependent foods to demanding variety at all times may result in an increase in the amount of transport, which uses energy, albeit a relatively small amount globally.

From an environmental perspective, this movement of foodstuffs can also cause increased fuel use for the production of fertiliser to replace exported nutrients. However, the production of high-value foods in developing countries may make both economic and humanitarian sense if it provides a better livelihood for those regions than would subsistence farming. Paradoxically, in China these subsistence and near-subsistence farmers may be the first to suffer from the environmental effects of changing agriculture.

Half a century after Mao Zedong's 'Great Leap Forward' brought irrigation to the arid grasslands in this remote corner of northwest China, the government is giving up on its attempt to make a breadbasket out of what has increasingly become a stretch of scrub and sand dunes.

In a problem that is pervasive in much of China, over-farming has drawn down the water table so low that desert is overtaking farmland. Authorities have ordered farmers here in Gansu province to vacate their properties over the next 3½ years, and will replace 20 villages with newly planted grass in a final effort to halt the advance of the Tengger and Badain Jaran deserts.

'I don't want to move,' said Chen Ying, 58, sitting in a sparsely furnished bedroom dominated by a red, wall-sized poster of Mao, the communist founding father who sought to catapult Chinese farming and industry into modernity with the so-called Great Leap Forward.

'But if we keep using the groundwater, it will decline,' said Chen. 'We have to think about the next generation.'

It is not just Chen's home region that is at risk.

The relocation program is part of a larger plan to rein in China's expanding deserts, which now cover one-third of the country and continue to grow because of overgrazing, deforestation, urban sprawl and droughts. The shifting sands have swallowed thousands of Chinese villages along the fabled Silk Road and sparked a sharp increase in sandstorms; dust from China clouds the skies of South Korea and has been linked to respiratory problems in California.

Since 2001, China has spent nearly US$9 billion (euro6.8 billion) planting billions of trees, converting marginal farmland to forest and grasslands and enforcing logging and grazing bans. The policy is driven in part by concerns over food, as farmland yields not only to the deserts but also to pollution and economic development. China has less than 7 percent of the world's arable land with which to feed 1.3 billion people – more than 20 percent of the world's population. By comparison, the United States has 20 percent of the world's arable land to feed 5 percent of the population.

But the initiative is also a tacit admission by the government that the effort to feed the country at all costs may have backfired. Chen was just a child when the government turned the rugged grasslands on the edge of the Tengger into an oasis. In the 1950s, as part of Mao's scheme to boost food production, the government built the Hongyashan Reservoir in Gansu province with the goal of irrigating nearly 1 million acres (400,000 hectares).

But over the past two decades, new reservoirs were built farther up the Shiyang River, sapping the Hongyashan Reservoir. It even dried up in 2004 and is only about half full today. Farmers responded by digging thousands of wells, causing the water table to drop hundreds of feet and the soil to become contaminated with salt. Worried the desert could reach the city of Minqin, 35 miles (56 kilometers) away, authorities decided to return the land to its natural state.

'If the government does nothing, it is scared that the entire area will become a desert,' said Sun Qingwei, a desertification expert with the Chinese Academy of Sciences. 'There are alternative solutions like introducing new plant species or conserving water. But this is the quickest solution. The government can show the people they are doing something.'

Chen, a grizzled farmer who sports a Mao cap, blue coat and baggy, mud-spattered pants, has planted dozens of trees outside his home to prevent the desert dunes from overrunning his property. He also switched from wheat to less thirsty cotton and fennel. But he appears to have met his match in the government, which already banned the use of well water for irrigation and threatened to cut the electricity ahead of the scheduled move of his village later this year to a new location about 12 miles (19 kilometers) away.

Talk of the impending moves dominates the conversations of villagers, gathered around their coal-fired stoves to ward off the springtime chill. Most are reluctant to leave. Authorities are offering up to US$784 (euro589) per family to move 10,500 residents from Gansu Province, but the villagers don't trust the government to compensate them fairly. Their ancestors are buried on their land, and their crops continue to earn a tidy income, they say – even though the canals that once transported water to the area are bone-dry, and the wheat that thrived here is a distant memory.

'The government is taking this action against desertification, but we are the ones being forced to pay for this policy,' said Li Jianzhu, a father of three in the village of Waixi, whose population has dropped nearly two-thirds to 60 residents.

Throughout the province, treeless, wind-swept plains stretch for miles […] in all directions. Gone are the knee-high grasses and the Qingtu Lake, replaced by sands from the expanding Tengger and nearby Badain Jaran deserts and with soil scarred white from salt.

The only signs of civilization in many areas are the herds of sheep munching on thorn bushes, the clusters of mud and straw homes and the burial mounds. Billboards promoting the country's one-child policy compete with those pushing slogans like 'No Reclamation, No Overcultivation.' Many communities have been emptied altogether, leaving behind crumbling homes and empty courtyards.

The battle against deserts is playing out across much of western China. Desertification has caused as much as US$7 billion (euro5.3 billion) in annual economic losses, the China Daily reported. Over the past decade, Chinese deserts expanded at a rate of 950 square miles (2,460 square kilometers) a year, according to Wang Tao of the Chinese Academy of Sciences in Lanzhou.

'There are quite a few countries with this problem but none on the scale of China because it is so big,' said Lester Brown, president of Earth Policy Institute. 'You only have to go to northwest China and see that the numbers and size of dust storms are increasing.'

Expanding deserts have contributed to a nearly six-fold increase in sandstorms in the past 50 years to two dozen annually, Wang said.

Global warming will worsen the problem, as rising temperatures lead to widespread drought and melt most glaciers on the Tibetan Plateau, depriving lakes and rivers of a crucial water source, according to the U.N.-funded Intergovernmental Panel on Climate Change.

Hotter, drier land is more vulnerable to soil erosion, Wang said. 'This is the same problem the United States faced in the 1930s with the dust bowl.'

Global warming also threatens to make a huge dent in grain production, which Brown said has already slipped from 432 million tons in 1998 to 422 million tons in 2006 because of desertification. At the same time, grain consumption has risen about 4.4 million tons a year to 418 million tons, in part because of rising demand for beef, chicken and pork. The production declines have forced China to draw down its grain stocks, and eventually it will need to buy a massive 30–50 million tons a year on the world market, Brown said.

'It's not that they are likely to face famine in the next few years. But what they may face is rising food prices, and that can create political instability,' he said.

In Dongyun village, Wei Quangcai and his deaf wife may offer a glimpse of that future. Once part of a thriving village of 200 people in Gansu province, they are the only ones left after neighbors fled two years ago.

Walking past the empty homes, Wei, 58, recalls the days when his village hummed with farmers chatting over a game of cards and the school was packed with children. Now, the only sounds are the wind whipping through the empty doorways. His son has left for a job in Beijing over his objections.

'We're the last people,' Wei said. 'It is lonely. It would be better if my son lived with us. But if he did, he wouldn't be able to find a wife.'

(Sina English, 2007)

Will China, and the rest of the world, choose diets that are efficiently produced, in terms of food output per hectare of land and with minimal environmental damage? The evidence so far is that decisions about diet are being made by an urban population increasingly remote from the realities of food production.

Summary of Section 9

The environmental implications of changes in China's diet and in the lifestyle of its people have been examined. The form of agricultural production now used may be less sustainable than older forms, but economic pressures all encourage this form of production. Pollution and demands for water associated with Chinese industrialisation are likely to damage the food production capacity of the land.

You should now be able to discuss the effects of changes in human diet on the numbers of people that can potentially be fed across the world.

10 Conclusion

There are several lessons in this for all of us, but they may not be comfortable. A diet based largely on grains, with a small amount of meat, like the traditional Chinese form, has much to recommend it. Yet in the UK and USA the demand for meat is already high, and the concept of seasonally varied diets has largely disappeared. Seasonal foodstuffs are either freighted in from different *agroclimatic zones*, or artificial environments such as greenhouses are used to extend the (temperature-dependent) growing seasons. Given the widespread recognition of the problems of obesity and other health issues associated with high meat consumption in the West, there does seem to be a strong case for a more grain-based diet, supplemented with smaller amounts of livestock products derived either from uncultivable land or food wastes. However, the economic signals that might achieve this do not currently seem to be present. Even in China, economic forces are becoming paramount, as the following quote suggests.

> He Kaiyin, an expert on rural issues from Anhui, said it was reasonable to aggregate the land for better utilization, as much farmland remained idle and irrigation and other rural infrastructure deteriorated after farmers swarmed into cities.
>
> About 60 percent of the village's 133.3 ha of farmland has been leased and re-divided into larger patches for industrial production of mushrooms, flowers, grapes or livestock.
>
> Yan Deyou, once the head of Xiaogang Village, is now cultivating a 12 ha vineyard, which he said 'can bring a profit 10 times that of grain farming.'
>
> He added: 'This year, about 40 hectares of the leased farmland in my village have been pooled to grow grapes, which has facilitated centralized management and made it easy to fertilize, water and remove pests from the land.'
>
> In 2007, the per capita annual income in Xiaogang exceeded the national rural average of 4,140 yuan to reach 6,000 yuan. 'That could not happen if each family was still working on its small piece of land separately,' said Shen Hao, the party chief of the Xiaogang Village.
>
> *(Sina English, 2008)*

The original reason for redistribution of land was to increase efficiency of production of food per unit of inputs such as land, labour and nutrients, but the products actually grown (grapes, flowers and livestock) were chosen in response to economic measures, rather than to needs for food. We should remember that those economic measures are the expression of our food purchasing decisions. Economically rational producers will produce what we will buy, not what is best for our health or what causes least environmental impact. Are we prepared, or able, to change our behaviours and alter our diet to something closer to that of last century's Chinese peasants, and possibly to carry out more of the preparation of foods ourselves? Without such change, it is unlikely that the much-vaunted free market will send signals to farmers to produce foodstuffs in ways that supply nutritional needs with minimal environmental impact, rather than in ways dictated purely by consumer preferences.

SAQ 2.6   Environmental effects of diet

Look back at my day's food in SAQ 2.1. What factors associated with this affect its environmental impact? Suggest how this impact could be reduced.

Summary of Part 2

China demonstrates graphically the nature and effect of changes in food production that have occurred as a result of political and social change. Human aspirations, economic development and political dogma have all affected the ways in which food is produced and consumed. Urbanisation and changes in diet cause major changes in methods of food production and these have environmental effects locally and globally. This raises questions about the nature of the diets we choose if we are to feed the world's population without major environmental damage.

After completing Part 2 you should be able to:

- Describe the basic nutritional requirements of humans, carry out calculations about dietary energy supply and comment on the form and adequacy of a particular diet.

- Describe the changes in diet, and food production in China in the twentieth century.

- Outline the major processes of crop and animal production involved in providing food for humans and recognise the importance of plant nutrient supply and cycling in food systems.

- Recognise some of the limits of published sources of information, and critically examine data presented as graphs or tables.

- Outline some important physiological, economic and political factors that affect the methods of agricultural production used in the world.

- Discuss the relationship between human food choice, food production methods and environmental issues.

Answers to SAQs

SAQ 2.1

(a) According to Table 2.4 I need 9.3 MJ per day. I think I am probably more active than this suggests, so probably need closer to 10 MJ.

(b) While this diet is relatively simple, the amount of meat consumed is certainly greater than in the Chinese example, and there is greater variety in terms of different forms of staple (porridge, bread, potatoes, wholemeal pie crust). The amount of fruit consumed (though probably less than currently recommended!) is still greater than in 1920s China.

(c) All items would supply some food energy, but the main sources were probably the staples and the meat. Butter on the sandwich and possibly in the pie crust, any fat in the yoghurt and sugar in the fruit pie would also supply energy. Protein would come mainly from the staples and the meat.

SAQ 2.2

From the description in Block 4, it appears that the Amazonian peoples were much less concerned with closed nutrient cycles than were the Chinese. In 'slash and burn', the ash from burning supplied phosphorus and potassium, but subsequent crops had to rely on the nitrogen that was present in the soil. The role of livestock in the indigenous systems was similar, acting mainly as scavengers, but in the subsequent ranching system their role was purely economic.

In the Chinese case, the local ecology was strictly controlled by human activity, and the landscape was far removed from its 'natural' state. The indigenous Amazonian peoples lived in a much less human-dominated system, but again, this was changing rapidly as the forest was removed for ranching or arable production.

SAQ 2.3

The biggest strength of the policy was probably that it ensured a basic supply of grain to supply the bulk of energy needs for all people. The organisation of the brigades should have ensured that effective use was made of available land and machinery. However, this concentration on grain production in unsuitable areas probably caused damage to soils. The attempt to impose industrial production on rural areas was an unmitigated disaster, taking effort away from food production and causing direct damage to the land through deforestation. Overall, more environmental damage was probably caused by the brigade system than in the earlier situation.

SAQ 2.4

Figure 2.18 suggests that there was no economic gain from applying more than about 260 kg of fertiliser per hectare because the average application rate did not go above this figure. So the value of the additional yield obtained by using, say, 260 kg per hectare rather than 259 kg per hectare should be equal to the cost of the additional 1 kg of fertiliser. Suppose that adding that extra kilogram of fertiliser per hectare increased grain yield by 10 kg per hectare; this would be economically rational if a kilogram of grain was worth at least one tenth of the cost of one kilogram of fertiliser.

SAQ 2.5

The major change appears to be a significant decrease in direct grain consumption, with an increase in animal products, itself causing an increase in indirect grain consumption. Given that feeding grain to livestock may result in less human food being produced per unit of grain than through its direct consumption, the increase in meat consumption is likely to make it more difficult to feed a given population. To get that extra grain, more land might have to be brought into cultivation, with possible dangers of erosion etc., or (as has actually happened) imports of feed grains need to increase.

SAQ 2.6

The environmental impact of food items depends critically on their original source, the agricultural systems used to produce them and the extent and nature of the processing that they have undergone. To take the example of the beef casserole, if the beef was imported into the UK from Brazil (which, as it happens, it wasn't!) then from what you have learned in Block 4, its environmental impact would be high, with the associated forest clearance for ranching or soya production for intensive feedlot systems. Refrigerated transport from South America to Europe would also add to the impact. In contrast, if the beef were locally reared on largely uncultivable land in Scotland, with limited additional grain feed to increase growth rate, its impact is probably very low. Cooking the casserole uses fuel. It's possible that a pre-prepared casserole, cooked in large-scale, energy-efficient plant might have less energy cost, although the packaging, possibly longer chilled storage and cost of reheating would probably negate this.

Similar arguments would relate to the fruit pie, regarding where and how the ingredients were produced, how efficiently it was cooked and stored. Fruit produced and used from my garden during the local short growing season would have less impact than fruit airfreighted from Africa or New Zealand. However, out of season, it has been suggested that the carbon costs of special storage of fruits in the UK outweighs the carbon cost of freighting seasonal produce from New Zealand.

The lesson from this is that reducing the environmental impact of your food requires careful balancing of different aspects, but is not impossible.

References

Agrifoodasia (n.d.) *Livestock*, http://www.agrifoodasia.com/English/ind_sectors/livestock. htm (Accessed 23 July 2009).

Buck, J.L. (1930) *Chinese Farm Economy*, University of Chicago Press.

Buck, J.L. (1937) *Land Utilisation in China*, Shanghai, Commercial Press.

Croll, E. (1983) *The Family Rice Bowl*, London, Zed Press.

Dong Fengxia and Fuller, F.H. (2007) 'Changing diets in China's cities: empirical fact or urban legend?', *Working Paper 06-WP 437*, Center for Agricultural and Rural Development, Iowa State University, http://www.card.iastate.edu/publications/synopsis. aspx?id=1031 (Accessed 23 July 2009).

Gao Chao, Sun Bo and Zhang Tao-Lin (2006) 'Sustainable nutrient management in Chinese agriculture: challenges and perspective', *Pedosphere*, vol. 16, pp. 253–63.

Gifford, R. (2008) 'Yellow river blues', *Prospect*, vol. 148 July, pp. 48–51.

Heilig, G.K. (1999) *ChinaFood. Can China Feed Itself?* Laxenburg, IIASA.

Li Huizi and Cheng Yunjie (2007) *Food Revolution in Chinese Army*, http://english.sina. com/china/1/2007/1004/127360.html (Accessed 23 July 2009).

McCance, R. and Widdowson, E. (1978) *The Composition of Foods*, 4th revised edition, Paul, A.A. and Southgate, D.A.T., London, HMSO.

Mann, C.C. (2008) 'Our good Earth', *National Geographic*, September, pp. 88–106.

Marchaim, U. (1992) 'Biogas process for sustainable development', FAO Agricultural Services, Bulletin No. 95.

Mingkui Cao, Shijun Ma and Chunru Han (1995) 'Potential productivity and human carrying capacity of an agro-ecosystem: an analysis of food production potential of China', *Agricultural Systems*, vol. 47, pp. 387–414.

Mottram, R.F. (1979) *Human Nutrition* (3rd edition), London, Edward Arnold.

Needham, J. (1984) *Science and Civilisation in China*, Volume 6: Biology and Biological Technology, Part II, Agriculture, by Bray, F., Cambridge, Cambridge University Press.

Shuyan Cao, Gaodi Xie and Lin Zhen (2008) 'Total embodied energy requirements and its decomposition in China's agricultural sector', *Ecological Economics*, [online]. Accessed 8 September, 2009.

Sina English (2007) 'Expanding deserts in China forcing farmers from fields, sending sandstorms across Pacific', Associated Press 19 June, http://english.sina.com/ china/p/1/2007/0619/115571.html (Accessed 23 July 2009).

Sina English (2008) 'Chinese peasants explore new path to development', 2 October, http://english.sina.com/china/2008/1001/189532.html (Accessed 23 July 2009).

United States Environmental Protection Agency (2009) 'How much methane is produced by livestock?', http://www.epa.gov/methane/rlep/faq.html (Accessed January 2009).

Vavilov, N.I. (1992) *Origin and Geography of Cultivated Plants*, Cambridge, Cambridge University Press.

Xiaoping Weng and Caballero, B. (2007) *Obesity and its Related Diseases in China*, New York, Cambria Press.

Yen, S.T., Cheng Fang and Shew-Jiuan Su (2004) 'Household food demand in urban China: a censored system approach', *Journal of Comparative Economics*, vol. 32, pp. 564–85.

Zhou Ke, Cao Xia and Tan Baiping (2008) 'Toward an improved legislative framework for China's land degradation control', *Natural Resources Forum*, vol. 32, pp. 11–24.

Part 3
Made in China

James Warren

Introduction

1

Part 3 continues the story you were introduced to in Parts 1 and 2. It explores in more depth the notion of China as the workshop of the world and it looks at how Chinese consumption patterns are changing beyond food. It also puts 'us' in the picture, as many of the purchases we make come from China; they are either made there or assembled there. It explores what things the Chinese make for the rest of the world as well as for themselves. Our consumption fuels Chinese productivity and industrial growth and, in turn, the growing consumption of the Chinese themselves. But this growth comes at a high cost, not only in terms of pure resource usage, but also in terms of pollution and the generation of waste, and we explore this. There is an interesting human story to be told here about how the Chinese entrepreneurial spirit, coupled with hard work, turns waste into money. We will spend some time with the street recyclers of Chinese cities, many of them migrants from the countryside. Finally, we look to the future and, through the motif of the Chinese dragon, consider three possible scenarios for China's future development.

Section 2 considers how China has become the workshop of the world and picks up the story introduced in Part 1. It focuses largely on 'manufacturing production' and assembly and its importance in and outside China.

Section 3 addresses how Chinese manufacturing meets global demand for cheap goods around the world. I explore how we as Western consumers drive the great China 'machine' by our demand for cheap goods. I look at some of the 'things' that we import (into the UK) from China. Such huge demand has fuelled economic growth in China and this has in turn generated increases in Chinese consumption. I discuss the big three items purchased by the Chinese as a so-called 'one-time purchase'. What we learn is that the Chinese are maturing as consumers, partly as a result of their growing wealth, increasing leisure time and ageing demographic; as the nation begins to become predominantly older many will be looking forward to their retirement. Their leisure time might include travel outside China, although an ageing China will also require greater resources dedicated to the care of the elderly.

Section 4 addresses the increased demand for raw materials to produce the goods consumed both outside and inside China. It looks at how global demand for Chinese manufactured goods has meant huge increases in consumption of energy and other resources such as water. When we consume goods produced in another country, the emissions from the production of that good (e.g. the manufacturing process) are said to be embedded in that traded good. This prompts the question of who is responsible for all the embedded carbon in our DVD players, PCs, flat screen TVs, clothing, etc. Should it be in China where it was made? Or perhaps it should be in the country to where it was exported and used during its lifetime.

Section 5 demonstrates that this matter is further complicated because these products ultimately become waste and need to be disposed of at the end of their useful life. Many of these 'durables' go back to China for reprocessing, and thus the item 'returns' home in one sense. It may seem rather ironic that we buy what we want (at prices we demand), and by doing so we simply shift the burden of the carbon- and waste-intensive phases of the product to wherever labour is readily available and waste processing regulations are less stringent. These conditions lead to a thriving market for disposed white and electronic goods. By looking at the street recyclers of China's cities, this section also explores how Chinese entrepreneurial spirit, coupled with hard work, has turned waste into a business.

Section 6 looks at three very different potential scenarios for China's future and explores some of the implications of these for the wider world.

The workshop of the world   2

You should by now have some feeling for the vast area of China, its large population, its migration trends, and how it nourished itself both historically and more recently. The block now turns towards the production systems for goods within China and how some of these systems are changing people's lives for the better and perhaps the planet for the worse. This section will begin to examine production, manufacturing and assembly of goods in order to appreciate the particular advantages that China offers to manufacturing and to appreciate the global reach of its goods.

Here I use the term *goods* to mean any item which can be purchased by the majority of consumers to be used in a useful way. ***Durable goods*** are those kinds of commodities like appliances that generate benefits over a substantial period of time. ***Non-durable goods*** are commodities like food and clothing, which are consumed over a relatively short period of time. You might consider these as 'consumables' in the office, or as perishables in the kitchen. As we saw in Jackie's household, migration led to a very different set of circumstances which allowed for relatively large changes in the household consumption and the way she viewed goods.

From an economic perspective, the household is composed of consumers, and each of these individuals consumes goods and *services*, but in turn each working adult also produces some form of goods (and services) in their job or at home. Thus a basic cycle of production and consumption of goods is formed and this creates opportunities. Creation of all consumer goods needs resources such as raw materials, energy, water, land and labour to maintain production and sustain output. This in turn creates potential for environmental damage through unwanted outputs. These may be in the form of polluted water, air or soil, or creation of hazardous or other wastes. The production systems may also generate unsightly buildings and create offensive noise or many other, less tangible outputs such as social disruption of established towns or villages.

So firstly let us turn to investigating the idea of China as the workshop of the world.

2.1   Why is everything made in China?

In more than one way China has become, and continues to be, the workshop of the world. By this I mean that China is producing more of our consumer goods than ever before. Think back to Activity 1.4 where you found typical things in your household 'made in China'. You may have identified these by their labels similar to that shown in Figure 3.1.

Figure 3.1 A typical bar code and label for a product which was produced in China

Since joining the World Trade Organization (WTO) in 2001, China has rapidly become an economic force, doubling its share of global manufacturing output and creating a commodity-market boom. Every day thousands of shipping containers arrive in Europe from China, filled with goods to meet our consumer demands.

Activity 3.1   Thinking about how imported goods are made

Thinking back to Part 1, suggest some reasons why so many of our things are made in China. To answer this, you will need to consider how these things are produced.

Discussion

In many cases, in my household, the proportion of stuff 'made in China' was close to 90% of the things I counted. Some ideas I came up with are:

- Is this a product which requires a lot of manual labour or labour which may be more affordable in China?

- Is this a product which is distinctly Chinese and only made there, such as a food product like soy sauce?

- Is the product dependent on materials only available in China?

The drivers for China to become the workshop of the world are complex, and have evolved over time. Many business analysts have been using the term '*China Price*' to describe the effect of extremely low prices that Chinese manufacturers offer. In many cases these prices are about 50% lower than the typical global price. This block cannot attempt to explain in detail how China got to the point where it is today, but in brief, some of this can be attributed to a specific set of factors (Navarro, 2007):

- lower wage costs
- good access to raw materials and sub-components
- market reforms providing export subsidies or land subsidies
- network clustering within China (this means locating suppliers or related businesses physically close to the main manufacturer)
- very large scales of economy – traditionally called *economies of scale*
- a well-disciplined and educated workforce.

Lower wage costs contribute to the China Price effect by lowering the overall cost of production. The wage level of a typical American labourer in 2007 was approximately $17 per hour compared with China, where it was just under $2 per hour (*The Economist*, 2008, p. 72). Manufacturers seek out the lowest wage labour market, and many are prepared to relocate to factories outside their own country to access this. This is helped by the WTO, the international body which promotes free trade by reducing trade barriers between countries. China's government also offers a large range of subsidies to manufacturing companies that produce for export, such as subsidised costs for energy, water, capital and land, and VAT (value-added tax) rebates on many exports. The lower wage costs coupled with these incentives and the large scale of factories in China is attractive for manufacturers. Migration will continue to enlarge a workforce of some 500 million factory workers who were formerly peasant farmers. To give you an idea of the size of this new workforce, the total of 500 million workers is equivalent to the current workforces of the Euro zone countries and the United States combined. The majority of these workers are very eager to learn and adapt their skills within the workplace and are deemed by Navarro to be a high-quality workforce.

Another factor that is attractive to manufacturers is the practice of locating all or most of the key components and/or enterprises in one supply chain for a particular product in close proximity. This is called *industrial network clustering*, and can lead to substantial gains in many areas.

Activity 3.2   Business clusters in China

Why do you think there are business advantages in using clustering? Do you think there are any environmental benefits to this practice?

Discussion

Some potential savings in clustering stem from cutting transportation costs. Clusters also reduce searching costs; these are costs that companies bear in order to find suppliers who can provide components for their process. All of these clustering effects have the potential to reduce emissions by reducing transport vehicle miles, generally from diesel- and petrol-powered vehicles, and may also thus help to improve global, but not necessarily local, air quality.

Clustering in China takes the form of 'supply chain cities' that tend to focus on a single product or set of products:

> For example, in the Pearl River Delta area […] Huizou has emerged as the world's largest producer of laser diodes and as a leading DVD producer as well. Foshan and Shunde are major hubs for appliances such as washing machines, microwave ovens, and refrigerators. Foshan is home to nearly 3.5 million people in the Guangdong province. Shunde is one of the five districts in Foshan and was historically known for its fine porcelain ware. Hongmei focuses on textile and leather-related products, Leilu for bicycles, and so on.

(Navarro, 2007)

In the UK, similar industrialised concentration existed historically, with examples such as steel in Sheffield, chain making in the Black Country and shoe production in Norwich and Northampton. Thus in China there are entire small cities dedicated to the state-of-the-art techniques in producing, for example, running shoes or trainers. A place like this is sometimes known colloquially as 'sneakerville' or similar. There are thousands of these hubs becoming product centres known as dishwasherville, furnitureville and televisionville.

Navarro also notes that there are other activities which help drive down the prices. These include an undervalued currency, making exports cheaper than they would otherwise be, and counterfeiting and piracy, which have avoided original research and development costs for products and the need for marketing budgets. All of these factors combine to drive down production costs and offer a very low price for consumers.

One way of tracking the success of the Chinese economy is to look at how UK imports from China have grown. Figure 3.2 records the value of

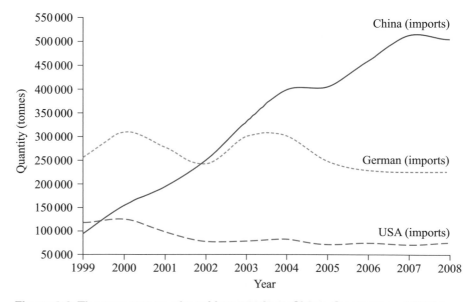

Figure 3.2 The percentage of total imports from China, Germany and USA to the UK over time. *Source: UK Trade Info, cited in Simms et al., 2007, p. 13*

electrical goods imported into the UK from China, Germany and the USA. As you can see, Chinese electrical imports have outstripped those from Germany and the USA since 2002.

To summarise the story so far, the huge growth of exports from China to many other parts of the world has been fuelled by the relatively low wages of Chinese workers, which were partly driven by the migration considered in Part 1. These lower costs of labour help manufacturers drive down the overall costs of products, together with tax advantages and subsidies offered by the Chinese government and the deliberate undervaluing of the Chinese currency.

One way of understanding this complex array of interacting forces is to use a multiple cause diagram (Figure 3.3), which can help by giving a visual summary of what is going on.

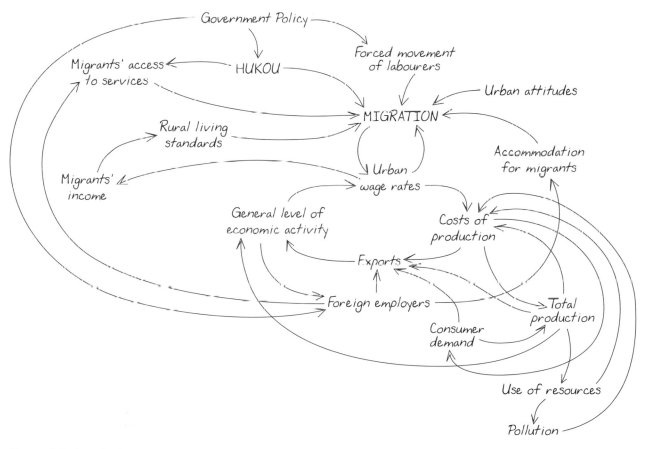

Figure 3.3 A multiple cause diagram showing some of the major interactions between migration, economic activity, total production levels and consumer demand

Figure 3.3 illustrates the wide variety of possible links between some of the major trends in China with respect to China's manufacturing boom. The diagram shows that as consumers demand more goods there is a direct effect on the overall production level. These consumers include both internal (Chinese) and external (e.g. British, European or American) consumers, with the external consumers affecting the level of exports. The total level of production in turn draws in resources and also creates pollution and other *externalities*. These are side effects which occur from certain types of activities and can be either negative or positive. They are defined in more detail later in this part in respect to life cycle analysis.

Box 3.1   Externalities

Externalities are those side effects that arise from undertaking a certain activity, usually economic, but they affect someone else not directly involved in the activity. Externalities are therefore not 'paid for' in the actual price of the goods, but in some cases they may be positive. Smoke from factories may stain homes and buildings nearby, and clean up of this has to be paid for by the city through the collection of taxes. Similar arguments can be made about air pollution. A positive externality – a benefit – could occur when a beekeeper's bees help pollinate nearby plants or fruit trees. The beekeeper is mainly interested in having healthy bees and getting a good crop of honey but others around him also benefit, without paying, from the bees' activities. Equally, there can be some examples of manufacturing-related externalities which are most certainly positive. Consider improved local transport infrastructure, put in place to facilitate movement of goods but also benefiting the rest of the local population. There may also be wider benefits to the economy at large – more taxes paid so more public spending possible, developing a highly skilled workforce and the potential for a feeling of local pride in the goods produced. As you can see, it is difficult to place a cash value on things like pride, better access and skills.

Although I have referred to China as 'the workshop of the world', in many cases much of the work involves the assembly of components, some of which are not made in China. For example, the processing and assembly of imported parts and components now accounts for more than half of all exports (Ziegler, 2007). A large majority of the sub-components are being assembled elsewhere and shipped to China for assembly. Imports account for 34% of total GDP and are distributed as follows: electrical machinery and semiconductors (19.7%), petroleum and petroleum products (7.9%), computers (5.3%), iron and steel (4.2%).

Levono (China's largest domestic computer firm) buys in many of the very difficult to manufacture or incredibly precise sub-components from outside China. This also means that some of the most complex sub-components, like the motherboard, command the highest levels of cost and profit as a total percentage of the computer and that to some extent China relies on somebody else's exports. By *outsourcing*, costs can be lowered. These lower production costs translate to a computer price which is some US$20–30 less to make per unit. This may seem like good news for you and for me – I would never have imagined that a DVD player could sell in Europe for only £20–40! But it does come at a price, as some have argued that the level of externalities in the form of pollution, low labour wages and, for many, poor working conditions are all too high. This may leave one wondering if our levels of consumption of goods can be sustained indefinitely.

Summary of Section 2

In many ways, the rest of the world has benefited hugely from China's manufacturing boom in terms of material goods, but this growth does come with a price. However, before we look at the environmental price in particular, we need to understand more fully what things are made in China, and what things come from China to the UK.

3   Consumers of Chinese goods

In this section I consider the demand for Chinese goods from outside China. The world is hungry for cheap, Chinese manufactures, but what are we importing and how much? About 36% of China's total GDP can be attributed to exports of goods and services. The main exported goods, expressed as a percentage, are computers (14.7%), telecommunications equipment (11.5%), clothing (10.4%), and electrical machinery and semiconductors (10.0%) (OECD, 2005). In 2004 China became the largest exporter of information and communication technology (ICT) related products. These include items like laptop and notebook computers, desktop computers, portable digital assistants, mobile phones and DVD players, as shown in Table 3.1. This table shows how production of these items has grown substantially in the early years of the twenty-first century.

Table 3.1 Selected industrial production for some of China's main exports, 2001–2007

Industrial production	Year	
	2001	2007
Cars	704,000	4,797,800
Microcomputers (millions)	8.80	120.73
Mobile telephones (millions)	80.30	548.58
Integrated circuits (millions)	6,363	41,162
Air conditioners (thousands)	23,336	80,143
Washing machines (thousands)	13,416	40,051
Refrigerators (thousands)	13,513	43,971
Colour television sets (thousands)	40,937	84,780

Source: extracts from EIU Country Profile (China) 2007, Table 3.1, p. 62 (data originally from China Statistical Yearbook 2001 and 2008)

3.1 UK imports from China

Let us consider what one country, the UK, imports from China. Table 3.2 gives some idea of the main things that the UK imports from China and represents how we are dependent on China for many of our consumer goods.

Table 3.2 Top 10 imports from China to the UK by cost, weight and rank (2006)

Rank	Items	Cost (£ billions)	Weight (tonnes, thousands)
1	Baby carriages, toys, games, sporting goods	1.26	378.82
2	Furniture including bedding, mattresses, mattress supports, cushions and stuffed furnishings	1.03	589.65
3	Computer equipment and accessories	0.89	31.81
4	Telecommunications equipment, parts and accessories (including telephones, loudspeakers, TVs and radios)	0.85	46.73
5	Parts and accessories for hi-tech machinery	0.65	23.31
6	Domestic electrical and non-electrical equipment (including microwaves, dishwashers, shaving equipment and parts and accessories)	0.64	243.10
7	Footwear	0.53	107.87
8	Clothing, textile fabrics whether or not knitted or crocheted	0.49	55.45
9	Women's/girls' outer garments, undergarments, nightwear (textiles) not knitted or crocheted	0.45	49.32
10	Plastics	0.39	266.37
Totals	Total for Top 10 items	15.56	6426.86

Sources: data from UK Trade Info (2006), cited in Simms et al., 2007, Figure 4

Based on weight, the top three shown above are: furniture and toys/baby-related items, followed by plastics. The top items for cost are toys/baby/sports and games items, followed by furniture and then computing items. I interpret this to mean that we import a lot of furniture (about a tenth of all top 10 imports), that in general these items are probably large in size, heavy and relatively expensive. For plastics the total cost is the lowest overall even though the amount is the third highest, probably signifying that plastic products are relatively cheap by weight. I suspect, looking at the list, that the items ranked 3 and 4 are both relatively expensive and relatively heavy per item – although certainly not as heavy as mattresses. The table also includes white goods, which are ranked 6.

SAQ 3.1   Plastic, toys and games consumed per person

Given that the UK population was approximately 59.7 million at the end of 2005, with some 26.1 million households, calculate how much plastic, toys and games from China were consumed per person and per household using the values from Table 3.2.

In Figure 3.4 a typical American household from Ohio shows a large part of their oil-based polymers, or plastic-based items. Many of these items are, not surprisingly, toys, and all of them contain carbon in some form or another.

Figure 3.4 A typical household displaying some of their carbon in various items. *Source: National Geographic (2009)*

The precise values for any household will vary enormously. Obviously, a household without children would be unlikely to buy any toys, so the amount bought by those with children would be greater than the calculated 14.5 kg. Similarly, a newly formed household might buy more furniture than an older household where these items do not need to be replaced.

3.2   Consumers of Chinese goods in China

In the previous section I looked at how China had become the workshop or assembly line of the world and how the world's demand for cheap consumer goods had spurred this development. In this section we step into Chinese society and consider what Chinese consumers buy, for it is not only global demand that is driving the Chinese economy, but also domestic demand. China is the world's largest domestic market. Therefore, if we are to have a fully formed picture of Chinese production we need to understand what the 1.3 billion Chinese consumers have bought in the past, are buying today, and aspire to buy in the future. You might like to stop and think for a moment about the kinds of things your parents purchased as young adults compared with the kinds of things you purchased, or what your favourite toys were compared with those of children you know today.

Many of these topics are addressed in a long-term study undertaken by Elizabeth Croll (mentioned in Part 2), an academic who had visited China almost yearly since the 1970s, studying Chinese households and their buying behaviours. Her work (Croll, 2006) has documented the hopes and purchases of Chinese consumers over time. By identifying the big three purchases made by households, in Chinese known as 'san da jian' (三大件) which translates as 'three big items', Croll characterised how these consumables changed over time. Four historical periods can be identified in her study: the Socialist Revolution spanned from 1960 to the late 1970s followed by three phases of increasing consumerism. I have borrowed names for the other periods based on what consumers most wanted to purchase, and called the 1980–89 period Necessity Appliances, and the 1990s Middle Class Consumer. The final and current phase, from 1999 to the present day, has been called the The Chinese Dream and is characterised, as you will see, by the Super Big Three Items.

All of these periods need to be seen as overlapping with each other to some extent, and of course being different for families with varying spending levels which feed consumption. Consumption means the amount of money, or expenditure, that a household makes, or plans to make, and which is then spent on both durable and non-durable goods and services. These increasing demands for consumables present a problem, since there is a finite amount of some of the resources needed to manufacture and operate these goods. As shown in Block 1, these goods and services account for a significant portion of our overall emissions.

Table 3.3 may also help you visualise how these items overlap and fit together in time. Keep in mind that these categories are quite 'loose', such that each family, or household, will have different needs and incomes resulting in different consumer behaviours.

Table 3.3 The general progression of household consumer goods towards ever-increasing purchases in China over time

Dates or period	Big Item 1	Big Item 2	Big Item 3
Socialist Revolution 1960–1977	Bicycle	Wristwatch	Sewing machine
'Necessity Appliances', 1980–1989	Television	Washing machine	Refrigerator
'Middle Class Consumer', 1990–1998	Cookers, microwave	CD player, mobile phones, flat-screen TV, DVD player	Air conditioning
'The Chinese Dream', 1999 to present day	Personal computer	Automobile	Own home or flat

Source: adapted from Croll, 2006

Historically, the big three purchases are those items for which families tended to save for a long time and then buy as a one-off item. This was especially true during the Socialist years. These were items that were durable and meant to last for a very long time indeed; in many cases these consumables were repaired and passed on to others. In the Socialist period these three big purchases were a bicycle (Figure 3.5), a wristwatch and a sewing machine. Perhaps that isn't too surprising since getting to work or getting around, knowing the time and being able to make or repair a multitude of sewn household items were all key tasks for a successful working life. These items cost a lot compared to annual earnings, and were valued highly.

Figure 3.5 A man proudly displaying his Flying Pigeon bicycle in Hangzhou stands in front of a small business centre before heading off

Ownership of expensive items other than these was quite rare, being largely confined to those upper echelons of party leadership.

As Wang noted:

> With the exception of Chairman Mao himself, brands did not exist in China from 1949 till 1978, nor did the notion of mass consumerism. Between 1978 and 1990, at the dawning of the reform era, the market was dominated exclusively by state-owned trademarks (known in Chinese as *paizi*).

(Wang, 2008, pp. 25–26)

But with the economic reforms introduced by Deng Xiaoping from 1978, a more consumer-oriented society has emerged, calling for more product types from more brand makers, and the patterns of consumption have shifted. The big ('old') three can all still be found in most households, but as the household income has increased, together with product availability, so the big three items have changed. As the socialist revolution began to loosen its hold, the gleam and utility of white goods began to grab hold of the masses; this period may be referred to here as 'Necessity Appliances'. In historical order, the television set, the refrigerator and the washing machine became the hot items of the early 1980s for the affluent minority. These were in some cases black and white TVs which were powered by batteries cobbled together or by a single electrical power source in some rural villages, but it was in essence the beginning of a consumer revolution. A snapshot in time is shown here from Croll's work showing the large differences in ownership between rural and urban households in 1985. Table 3.4 shows the typical ownership levels of goods in Chinese households in 1985, expressed as the number of households owning a product per 100 households surveyed. In Figure 3.6 (for televisions only) the ownership for both rural and urban households is shown over a longer period of time.

Table 3.4 Proportion of ownership in both rural and urban households in China (1985) during the 'Necessity Appliances' period

Product	Rural ownership	Urban ownership
Fridge	Less than 1	6.6
TV (black and white)	11	67
TV (colour)	Less than 1	17
Cassette recorder	4	41
Washing machine	2	48
Electric fan	10	74

Source: Croll, 2006, p. 37

This revolution also brought with it electric fans, cassette players and cameras. These were the hotly sought-after 'smaller' items, at least in terms of their cost. But the rural–urban divide of ownership was stark, with many rural families owning many fewer, of the desired durables per 100 households.

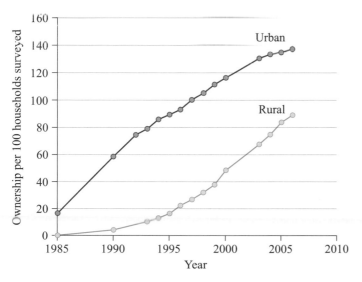

Figure 3.6 Colour television ownership in rural China reaches nearly 85% in 2005, whereas ownership in urban families reaches 100% in 1997. *Data from* **China Statistical Yearbook, 2005**

SAQ 3.2   Changes in rural and urban television ownership

How would you describe television ownership for both rural and urban households, especially after the year 2000?

After years of hardship and scarcity, particularly in the Chinese countryside, these purchases meant so much to rural households that a phrase was invented in Chinese to describe the number of big items available to a groom as dowry. Each desirable had a given number of legs, so a household might become known as a 20-legged household if it had a TV on a stand (four legs), and a washing machine, fridge, cooker and hi-fi, each also with four legs. A so-called 30- or 40-legged dowry would be particularly attractive in terms of desirables and probably meant that somebody in the family had a very well-paid job.

Televisions are an interesting consumer purchase for a variety of reasons; as a device they provide both entertainment and news. Televisions are also interesting in that if you compare the number of TVs in the rural households with the number of refrigerators, you may find an odd trend. For example, in 2005, only a quarter of all rural households owned a refrigerator (Figure 3.7) whereas more than 75% owned TVs. This is perhaps partly explained by what you learnt in Part 2, that cold storage only becomes essential with a broader diet, and rural areas were still eating relatively traditional foods to a large extent.

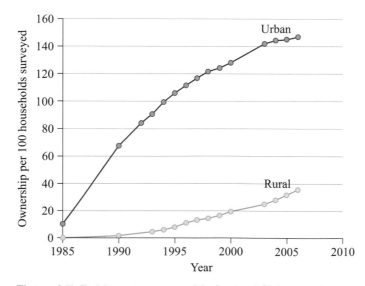

Figure 3.7 Refrigerator ownership in rural China reaches nearly 25% in 2005 whereas for their urban counterparts it is more than 90%. *Data from* China Statistical Yearbook, 2005

Jing Wang, in her book on brands and consumption patterns in China (Wang, 2008, pp. 19–20) has further defined Chinese consumers. She split them as follows, with the brackets indicating what percentage of total consumers that segment contributes:

- Generation Y, born after 1989 but before 2000 (about 15%, aged 8–19 in 2008)
- Generation X, born between 1977 and 1989 (23%)
- Chinese baby boomers, born between 1961 and 1976 (44%)
- The Cultural Revolution generation, born between 1945 and 1960 (33%).

These generational segmentations are important in Wang's view as they help us to understand what motivates different groups of people to consume. Her view is that clearly different households purchase different things and, following on from this, these items will require different amounts of resource to operate. Her views also help us to understand how Chinese factories differentiate product research and development for different segments of the Chinese consumer market. Note that the Chinese baby boomers will represent the largest future share in the market, and that their greater spending power will lead to interesting consumption trends. Currently, on a per capita basis, the electricity consumption level in China is about a quarter of that in Germany. We might be worried that if all individuals in China had the same consumption rate as an individual in a 'typical' European country, then total energy demand would increase significantly. If the demand leapt to American levels, China would need eight times more electricity per person to meet their needs (Wagner, 2008). We might expect that China, being quite hot in the summer, might follow an American-style consumption path which relies heavily on air conditioning. Clearly, certain devices draw much more energy than others, and the proliferation of appliances and devices means that certain homes consume more energy.

Two famous examples from the Chinese company Haier follow (see Box 3.2); these provide some insight into the industrial mechanisms at play in the Chinese appliance market in the 'Necessity Appliances' period of the 1980s. Both of these examples solved a certain market need for Chinese families, and yet they also tend to increase overall energy consumption.

Box 3.2   Big Yam and Little Prince

Big Yam

Haier is probably the leading Chinese made appliance and white good manufacturer. Haier means 'higher' in its English slogan and was chosen purposefully to capture the meaning of going higher and higher in pursuit of perfection in manufacturing. Zero defects and many other key performance indicators and processes have been implemented in all of their factories as they strive to become a national brand.

Haier had been pushing its products into the interior of China for some time, but it began getting many complaints from rural consumers living in the southwest. The majority were complaining about the poor quality of the water pipes in their washing machines. A team was sent to investigate the problems they faced and to help settle the grievances. The team quickly found that the main problem was that the pipes had become blocked by yam skins because peasants had used the machines to wash their yams. Instead of trying to change the behaviour of those washing their yams, when the machine was designed for clothes, the lead executive at Haier made a strategic move. He asked the team to design a new machine with enlarged pipes, a better drainage system and dual washing functions. The new product was named 'Big Yam' and has become the best selling washing machine in rural China.

Little Prince

Little Prince is another story of how a Chinese company has responded to the particular needs of the Chinese domestic consumer. Since the mid-1990s the work/life balance has tipped heavily towards work for those living in the cities and towns. This has meant that shopping was necessarily squeezed into a weekly trip rather than daily grocery shopping. But a weekly food shopping pattern required a bigger freezer to hold all the frozen items. However, the ever frugal Chinese consumer was not ready to part with their old refrigerator, even though they had an inadequate freezer compartment. Haier leapt at the chance to innovate and create a new item for this latent need; a low budget small freezer with a small space footprint. This was exactly what a typical overcrowded Beijing apartment needed – the Little Prince was born.

(Adapted from Wang, 2008, pp. 150–52)

Returning to the four periods of consumerism adapted from Croll, after the period of 'Necessity Appliances' came 'Middle Class Consumer', which moved away from appliances that provided leisure (TV), washed clothes (or root vegetables) and kept food cold (fridges) towards more sophisticated items like microwaves, cookers and air conditioning. The results of Croll's work are shown in Table 3.5, with ownership levels for a more recent survey (1996), again comparing urban and rural. Not all of the categories are the same as in previous tables, partly because of the changing nature of what kinds of goods are most desired, but the big three items of necessity remain, to a large extent, especially in rural areas. In the city household it shows very high penetration of many goods including TVs and, to a lesser extent, stereos, cameras and video players. Items with lower ownership included air conditioners (26% of all households), personal computer (4%) and video camera (2%), showing the beginning of the luxury wants becoming more apparent.

Table 3.5 Proportion of ownership in rural and urban households in China in 1996 – 'Middle Class Consumer' period		
Product	**Rural ownership**	**Urban ownership**
Fridge	~ 7	70
TV (black and white)	65	not stated
TV (colour)	23	93
Cassette recorder	31	73
Washing machine	21	91
Stereo (cassette)	not stated	27
Camera	2	32
Video player	0	~ 2 (estimated)

Sources: China Statistical Yearbook, 1997, cited in Croll, 2006, pp. 49–50

The period called Middle Class Consumer began to decline post-1996, but even at that time rural households were still some 10 years behind their urban counterparts in terms of consumption of goods and penetration of these goods into homes. But despite this lack of goods for some homes, Chinese consumers everywhere were looking forward to enjoying more luxury goods even if very few could actually afford them. The differences between rural and city households in both their durable goods ownership and incomes continues into the next period and to the present day to a large extent.

3.2.1   Living the Chinese Dream

As we turn to the fourth phase, which I have called The Chinese Dream, and in which many consider China to still be, a new set of big three items has begun to emerge. Lately these have been called 'chaoji san da jian' (超级三大件) or the super three big things. They represent China's desire for PC ownership (Figures 3.8 and 3.9), cars and private housing. Other items on the wish list included home furnishings of many descriptions, travel (for tourism) and recreational spending.

Figure 3.8 Bike delivery of desktop computers, with some friends hitching a ride

Figure 3.9 A return load of polystyrene foam inserts normally used to hold flat screen TVs or computer screens in place during shipping

Owning a car and house is still out of the reach of many, but may not be for as long as we might think. Obviously the purchase of a car or house is much bigger than the items we considered previously, but in many ways the pattern of consumption is the same. Car and house purchases are largely limited to the rich and super-rich in China, at the time of writing, owing to the high prices when compared with annual earnings. The purchase prices require some 7–10 years of capital accumulation (i.e. saving money), with even the cheapest cars, for example, costing some £12 000, with £4000 road tax per year. In 1995, even the cheapest two-bedroom house in Beijing cost about £100 000. At that time Croll reckoned that 1.7% of Beijing residents owned a car, typically a very basic saloon/hatchback. The vehicle price was about eight times the average salary and it was estimated that less than 1% of Chinese people could afford to buy a car. Others have estimated that being able to afford to buy a car does not really begin until monthly average income reaches approximately £600 per household and car ownership is much closer to attain financially.

So what do all these purchases mean in terms of energy and water use in China? The quote below paints a rather depressing picture of how China is changing, and beginning to follow a distinctly 'Western style' of economic growth. It would seem that quite a lot more energy and other resources would be needed to support this continued growth.

> Already the idea of China as a nation of cyclists seems quaint. Some 45,000 km of expressways have been built or are under construction. Through cheap petrol and other means, the government is supporting a domestic car industry, which it sees as an engine of future economic growth. The number of cars in China has leapt from just 4m in 2000 to 19m in 2005. That translates into eight cars per 1,000 people, compared with 500 cars per 1,000 in America. Goldman Sachs [a leading global financial services firm] thinks the figure will more than double by 2010 and reach over 130m by 2020. But even then China will still be way below American levels of car ownership today.

> *(The Economist, 2007)*

Summary of Section 3

We have seen that Chinese consumption is changing, both in total volume and in nature, and also in how people consume. China's population demographics are also changing, as each of the one-child-policy children begins to grow up. As the Chinese baby boomers and the Cultural Revolution generation age more, the number of people aged 40–64 with no dependents will grow from 265 million to nearly 325 million by around 2017–2020. All of these 'empty nesters' will create demand for even more leisure-related products and services. These might include huge opportunities for skin and health care, restaurants, hotels and travel within China and abroad. Yet living up to the Chinese 'dream' requires energy and resources and creates complex environmental issues. Thus, we now need to look at some of the unwanted outputs or externalities that accompany these changes, and the implications of these for the rest of the world. In the next section I will look specifically at the level of coal consumption which is necessary to power the many factories that supply goods to the Western world. A significant share of China's industrial energy is embedded in all of the products it eventually exports. In 2004 this was estimated to be 28% of the total energy consumed in the country (World Energy Outlook, 2007, p. 290). Coal extraction, consumption and future supply are important topics, since coal is the largest portion of China's total energy consumption.

After reading Section 3 you should now be more familiar with:

- how different types of consumer have distinctly different consumption needs and patterns
- the kinds of product that China makes, exports and consumes internally
- the way that energy and resource consumption tend to increase as a result of increased wealth at the family household level.

4 Feeding the factories – the consequences of consumption

Making and exporting goods needs energy and raw materials. In the case of energy, for China (Figure 3.10) this means coal, which in 2005 provided about 63% of China's primary energy demand (World Energy Outlook, 2007).

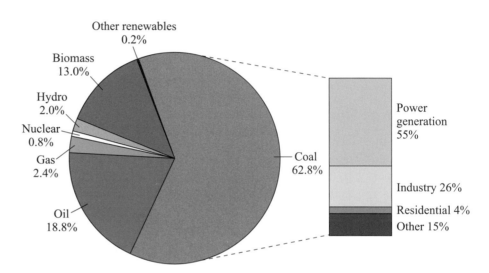

Figure 3.10 Chinese energy use 2005. Total energy demand is 1742 Mtoe. (Other 15% includes other energy sector, transport, services, agriculture, non-energy use and non-specified.) *Sources: BP Statistical Review, 2008; World Energy Outlook, 2007*

Oil provides about another 19% of energy demand, followed by biomass (13%), and some other smaller primary energy pathways make up the rest of China's overall energy usage.

Coal remains the chief provider of power generation in China and also a large portion of industrial power (Figure 3.11). Coal is also a huge contributor to emissions including mercury, sulphur dioxide and other toxins. So despite us depending on the 41% of global electricity which coal provides, it also creates 33% of global CO_2 (EarthTrends, 2005; McKibben, 2009). Each year the International Energy Agency (IEA) publishes its outlook for how energy is likely to be used over the next few years. The annual volume is used by many governments and others as a guide to potential energy trends. World Energy Outlook (2007) predicts the long-term energy demand for China using various sets of conditions. Their reference scenario assumes an annual energy growth rate of 3.2% from 2005 to 2030, meaning that China requires large increases in *primary energy*. Primary energy is the total amount of energy in the original energy source.

The main energy sources for China are fossil fuels (coal, oil and natural gas) so it would be reasonable to think that if most things continue, in terms of China's production dominance and the rest of the world's demand for goods, that China will invariably need more energy in some form.

Figure 3.11 The demand for coal in China for power has led to a worldwide concern about growing air pollution, dwindling fuel supplies and mining catastrophes.

China's energy consumption has been growing by about 4–5% per year over the last 20 years or so. This growth rate equates to a doubling time of about 22 years (see Part 1 Section 2) and if it continues then two main issues arise if China is to maintain its energy output. These are the prospect of very much higher CO_2 emissions, and security of supply. This huge demand must have some effect on the overall global supply of coal. Figure 3.12 shows the overall Chinese coal production and a well-known energy forecast. The Chinese have so far managed to keep ramping up production, but the future supply of their energy looks somewhat uncertain, especially if you think that a growth in energy consumption must be maintained. Is there enough coal for China to continue growing at such a substantial rate for the next 50 years? According to statistics produced by British Petroleum (BP Statistical Review, 2008), Chinese coal reserves in 2008 were nearly 115 billion tonnes. If Chinese consumption were to continue at its 2008 level, that would all be used up in a mere 41 years. There is a great gulf between China's future demand for coal and its ability to supply it from its own mines. Figure 3.12 illustrates this with a demand projection from the International Energy Agency and a projection of future production made by the German Energy Watch Group.

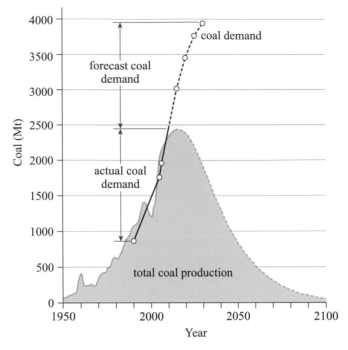

Figure 3.12 Coal production per year in China from 1950 to present day, with a future prediction to 2100. *Source: coal production – Energy Watch Group, 2007; coal demand – World Energy Outlook, 2007*

The coal consumption pattern in Figure 3.12 demonstrates what might be likely to happen. It predicts a peak in coal extraction over the next few years, and certainly before 2020. The prediction shows that 'easy' coal (e.g. coal from strip and deep mining tunnels) in China will be gone. The only contentious matter is exactly when this peak will occur, as not everyone is agreed on the date, but most are agreed that coal will run out by 2100, if not sooner, if demand stays at these relatively high levels.

But I need to stress how future predictions can vary a great deal between reports, and that they may all be wrong. In many cases we simply do not know when reserves of some resources like coal and oil are going to run out. There seems to be a growing consensus that fossil fuels will indeed reach a peak and then decline, but many different camps give very different dates. What may be argued, however, is whether we should be substituting renewable sources of energy for fossil fuels, and saving fossil fuels whenever practicable. These fossil fuels might be best saved for other uses, like making plastics, or for certain types of energy feedstocks where renewable energy resources might not work as well, or at all. We might also agree, or disagree, that all this fossil fuel, once combusted, will result in more greenhouse gas emissions unless there are very sensible ways to reduce those emissions, or store them indefinitely. Certainly, after having read Blocks 1–4 and considering the potential risks, it would seem that many individuals, scientists, organisations and nations are beginning to consider very seriously ways in which they can avoid and lower their overall CO_2 emissions.

When considering non-renewable resources (refer back to Block 3), it is not just peak coal or *peak oil* which presents a dilemma. We could also consider similar peaks such as peak uranium, peak copper and peak aluminium. Our imported goods, like DVD players, television sets and numerous white goods need plastics (produced from crude oils), housings and fittings (such as metal boxes to act as frames), and a variety of electronic sub-components and motors and compressors to operate (using silicon chips and associated wiring). China is currently consuming around a quarter of the copper and aluminium being globally extracted. China is also increasing its consumption in many other commodity areas, as shown in Figure 3.13.

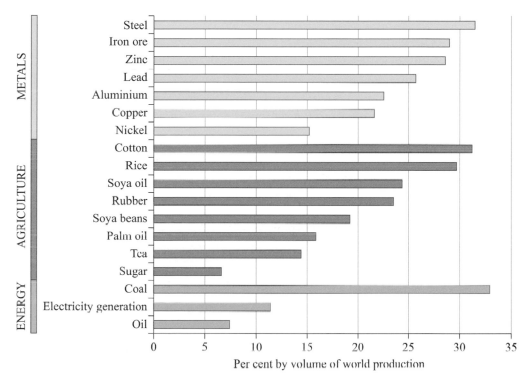

Figure 3.13 Primary commodity consumption in China; China is consuming a third of global coal, cotton and steel. *Source: Dancing with giants (note 2003 and 2005). Source: Winters and Yusuf, p. 16*

Copper is critical for the electrical wiring within computers, computer chips, cabling (in all white goods and electronic goods) as well as for cooling some devices as a heat sink to dissipate heat. We need aluminium for automobiles and aircraft bodies/airframes. If we assume that eventually many resources will become depleted or, like coal and oil, will become very much more costly to extract for smaller and smaller quantities, then perhaps we ought to treat every current resource we have much more sustainably. Certainly we will see large increases in costs of extraction, and presumably in prices to consumers, for consumables that rely on resources which are in great demand, as there will not be enough supplies to satisfy all consumers.

Of course, some of the materials demand might be met by the use of recycled materials, especially in the case of copper and iron, or even sub-components like memory chips from computers. In almost every case, reusing or recycling materials will result in an overall lower environmental impact compared with extracting raw materials.

The demand for raw materials has led China to reach out to other countries and continents, such as Australia for aluminium and Africa for oil and fossil fuels. As China grows ever larger in production terms it will require more inputs. These large demands may create instabilities in some places as countries compete for access to limited supplies. Although it is clearly China's right to develop, in a pathway it chooses, their development affects not only the Chinese, and their future generations, but also the next global generations.

Bottled Water – Who Needs It? is a short film about the production and manufacture of bottled water, explaining the basic steps in 'making' bottled water. The film is also quite specific in its perspective about how bottled water is an artefact of our continuing consumer lifestyle.

Please now watch Bottled Water – Who Needs It? on the DVD. It is about 8 minutes long. You can take notes whilst watching or listening or, if you prefer, simply watch it and let the main story soak in. To get all of the facts from the narrators you may need to consider watching it more than once. Bottled water, like the type you might see in any typical shop in Europe or the USA – or even urban China, is now a global consumer phenomenon. When you have watched the story, answer SAQ 3.3.

SAQ 3.3   Your thoughts on bottled water

Now that you have watched this video, what are the arguments for and against bottled water?

4.1   Unwanted outputs

The life cycle analysis (LCA) process considers all inputs and outputs that a product makes during its entire 'life' and is also sometimes informally referred to as cradle-to-grave analysis. It can be useful if we want to look at the possibilities of producing products that are less harmful to our environment. A rigorous LCA would look at each stage of the product life, including raw materials acquisition, manufacturing, distribution and retail, use, reuse, maintenance, recycling, waste management and/or end-of-life phases (Figure 3.14). The LCA process is particularly good for raising awareness of those additional undesirable outputs.

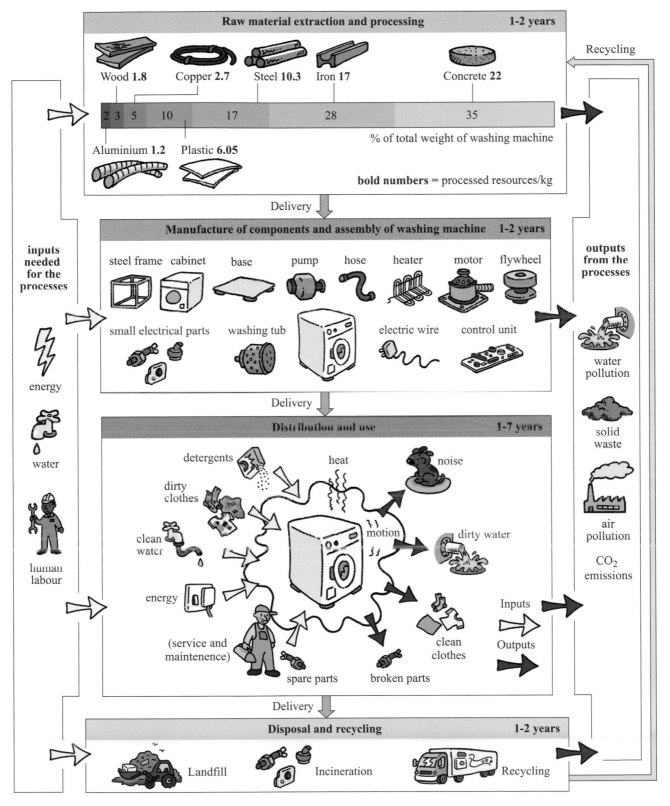

Figure 3.14 Environmental impacts of a typical clothes washing machine throughout its life cycle

LCA is a systems approach in that it catalogues all of the environmental impacts for each stage of the life cycle. It starts from the impacts due to extraction of the raw materials and then continues to include the processing of these. Many manufacturers are acutely aware of the energy, materials and water required to produce a good, and will attempt to reduce these inputs without sacrificing the function of the product. Reduction in manufacturing inputs makes good business sense, as lower inputs result in cost savings, which may result in higher profits for the firm, or lower prices for the public. Next there is the in-use phase, which tends to have relatively high impacts, especially if the good requires energy, water or some other form of maintenance. The final phase is the disposal and recycling. This phase may include dismantling for valuable components, depending on the item in question. Overall then, many studies have shown that the LCA for typical white goods attributes about 95% of the total impacts during the life. Another 3–4% of the impacts occur for the assembly, and extraction and disposal each account for about 1%.

Taking as an example a cotton shirt, we could consider that the material inputs are cotton cloth, thread and buttons. If we accept the assumption that every material originates from Earth, then we can follow cotton cloth back to its roots (no pun intended) as a cotton plant and a seed. It also had inputs such as water, sunlight and nutrients from the soil. As with the crops you saw in Part 2, it may have had a fair amount of fertiliser and energy applied in the form of mechanised agricultural equipment and associated processing. Cotton requires about 11 000 litres of water to produce 1 kg of cloth (Gleick, 2009), so it is a thirsty crop, and it also has one of the highest inputs of pesticide per hectare of any crop. Side effects of these represent another externality.

As further inputs to the production process, the dyed cotton cloth is transformed by human labour (skill to cut and hold the pieces), energy (in this case electricity) to power the sewing machines, and so on. In many cases a best guess must be made as to the exact amount of energy used, as many factories simply do not measure electricity for each process or sub-process. A best guess might involve using the annual energy consumption for a factory and then dividing this by the total number of units made that year to get energy consumed per shirt produced. Other inputs include food in the form of nutrition, some facilities, and lighting and heating in the factory. Many Chinese factories have baths, canteens and shops for their workers, as shown in Part 1. All of these facilities and inputs also create outputs in the form of waste, such as food packaging, sewerage, wasted heat and emissions from a power plant to produce the item. Another output is of course the finished and desired product.

This model of inputs, transformation to goods, and outputs may seem relatively simple but it can become very complex for many products, as you saw in Figure 3.14. This is especially true if one tries to catalogue all of the inputs and outputs during the production process. Yet this is not really the entire story, since the production phase of a shirt represents only a small part of the shirt's entire environmental impact over its whole life.

The operational phase of the shirt whilst in use may be some 2–3 years if used on a frequent basis. If worn less frequently but for a longer in-use phase, it is likely that the shirt will still have the same number of washes per lifetime. So how might we assign these inputs against the life of the shirt?

Part of the LCA process would be to undertake a *life cycle inventory* for a typical shirt. Since shirts are normally washed with other clothes, then it would be fairer to say that the inventory would look at an average of many items of clothing being washed in order to come up with a sensible lifetime list of inputs and outputs. Inputs would include water, soap, a washing machine and its energy and waste water generated. I have not included drying, but things become difficult if I begin to include some of my central heating for clothes drying (I hang my clothes above the radiator to dry). But the primary purpose of using the heating is to heat the house rather than dry my clothes, even though during the winter rain I am very grateful for dry clothing. In this respect the inventory would be much more straightforward (but less environmentally friendly!) if I had a drier and could directly calculate the energy for using that each time. The LCA can be fraught with difficulties when not knowing where to draw your boundary. In the case of my soap, should I count some of my car emissions to and from the shops to get the soap? I don't have a straightforward answer on how to resolve this dilemma; as in any environmental issue it is essential to be very clear about how you intend to quatify 'the issue' and report it.

Many of the finished consumer goods which we consider, especially those that require energy and water to operate, tend to have much higher outputs during their in-use phase of life. This phase is sometimes called the operational phase, as the product should be working, being used or operated.

SAQ 3.4   How much water does a shirt consume?

If we assume that a shirt is washed 50 times per year and lasts about 3 years, what is the total water 'consumed' by the shirt? You can assume that each wash consumes about 40 litres of water. What things have been unaccounted for, in your opinion?

Summary of Section 4

This section has attempted to give you an introduction to the complexity of finished consumer goods and some idea of how the industries that provide goods, as well as services, require many inputs. These inputs take many forms, such as human labour, energy and resources, but they also produce unwanted outputs that may lead to environment-related issues such as air pollution, waste water and contaminated land. Only by using rigorous methods such as LCA and understanding boundaries for products and their associated systems can we begin to have an informed debate and make choices with respect to some of these issues.

5 Dealing with waste

We have considered how China has become the workshop of the world as well as how the Chinese are becoming greater consumers themselves, from their changing diet (discussed in Part 2) to owning more household things. We have also considered the production cycle and the waste inputs and outputs that this can generate. We will now turn to the increasing problem of waste in China, and how it is being dealt with. We will consider mainly solid wastes.

Waste has increased in both the urban and rural areas, with varying levels of formalised waste collection systems in place (Figure 3.15), normally in the urban areas where city municipalities have taken a lead in waste management. We also explore informal waste systems and waste in rural China.

Figure 3.15 Keeping the streets clean is big business in China. In Beijing, nearly every back street has a large rubbish receptacle owing to the high number of *hutong* clearances

In the UK and Europe there is a clear distinction between recovery and recycling. Recovery usually refers to wastes that have had some 'value' recovered from them, so recovery refers to energy from waste and fuel manufacture, and recycling and composting. Recycling figures usually include composting, although increasingly these figures are reported individually or stated as combined recycling and composting figures. Thus you need to be careful when reading and comparing various figures for waste management for different countries, as some other countries use the terms recycling and recovery interchangeably. In their Environmental Permitting guidelines, Defra state that 'the key feature of a recovery operation is that its principal objective is to ensure that the waste serves a

Box 3.3   The waste hierarchy

The waste hierarchy is a management system for waste commonly applied to household wastes. It has a principal objective to protect the health of the public, but often this is forgotten in highly developed economies. Any strategy for waste management has three key objectives which are embodied in the hierarchy. These are minimising waste produced, make best use of waste that is produced, and minimise any immediate or future risk of pollution from waste management practices. We could view the hierarchy as five levels:

1   Reduce waste – don't create waste in the first place.

2   Reuse 'waste' – use products for a purpose more than one time.

3   Recycle waste – reprocess waste materials to be used for new products.

4   Recover waste – incinerate waste and recover energy for heat and power generation.

5   Dispose of waste – place waste in landfill which is not suitable for recovery, recycling or reuse.

(Adapted from Official Journal of the European Union, *2008)*

useful purpose by replacing other substances which would have had to be used for that purpose (thereby conserving natural resources)' (Defra, 2008).

Box 3.3 summarises the *waste hierarchy*.

5.1   Understanding waste in China

The composition of waste changes with time as a country grows and develops. This is because consumers earn more wealth, and their buying patterns change, leading to different types of things being purchased and eventually disposed of. Waste from poorer families in Beijing, for example, tends to be mainly organic matter (e.g. food-related scraps, some compostable paper), followed by ash and dirt. There is a very small amount of plastic, paper and glass, and rarely some metal items. This is in distinct contrast to that from a wealthier family, which is mainly paper-based waste, organic, plastic, glass and metals. Waste, as you will see, is also influenced by wastes that are imported and by waste that washes up on our shores, or blows into our regions.

Waste levels throughout the world are different for different countries, but generally range from just under 1 kg up to more than 2.5 kg of waste generated per person per day. China is at the lower end of the scale with a reported value of about 0.7 kg per person per day in 2002.

Waste also tends to grow in amounts over time as a country becomes 'wealthier', owing to increasing demands for raw materials and growing consumption by households. An example of 100 years of raw materials growth is shown in Figure 3.16 for the USA from 1900 to 2000. The major types of product are shown, along with strong economic 'dips' that tend to demonstrate reductions in materials flows.

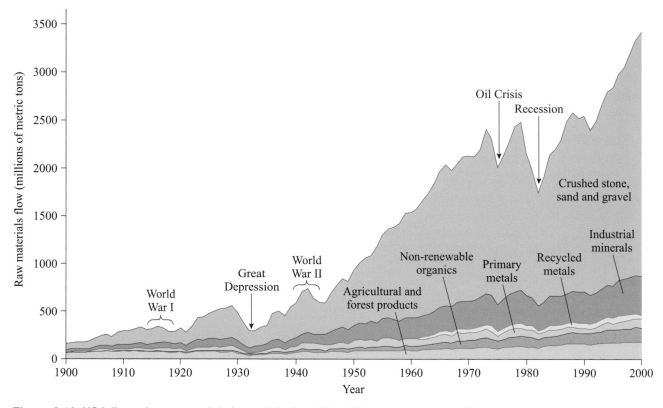

Figure 3.16 USA flow of raw materials by weight for 1900–2000, expressed in millions of metric tonnes.
Source: Wagner, 2001

You might have been somewhat surprised that from about the mid 1940s onward the major component of raw inputs has been crushed stone, sand and gravel. These are, and always have been to some extent, utilised for road-building programmes and other major construction programmes. These commodities in turn create wastes further 'downstream', and we would expect that China's large draw on commodities will also create wastes somewhere in the global system, but mainly in China itself. The USA, for example, generates some 1.9–2.2 kg waste per person per day (Wagner, 2001). With all of China's potential urban growth, one might also expect a continual level of consumption in quarried materials.

Figure 3.17 gives three different scenarios for China's municipal waste based on three predicted waste levels for the urban population of China. Clearly, this prediction only covers the urban dwellers. It would be expected that rural households would also generate waste; although these households may generate more overall, these wastes may be more organic in nature, as described above. The three scenarios considered modelled a starting waste value of 0.9 kg per person per day (similar to Slovakia or Poland), rising to a relatively low waste level (1.2 kg), which is similar to that for Japan, an expected waste (1.5 kg) value like Estonia, Sweden, or France and a high waste (1.8 kg) value like that of Luxembourg, Ireland, Cyprus or Denmark. Some of the waste generation and disposal processes, as you will shortly read about, are very different from those normally considered in developed countries. The next section will explore these so-called brownfield sites in more detail.

Brownfield landfill sites are landfill sites that are uncontrolled rubbish tips; they have no mechanisms for protecting the environment from the waste tipped into them. They are called 'brownfield' as the sites tend to create contaminated soil and water tables when rubbish is continually dumped with no safeguards such as impermeable liners or legislated controls on types and amounts of waste that can be dumped. The liquids leached from the rubbish sites can be very hazardous.

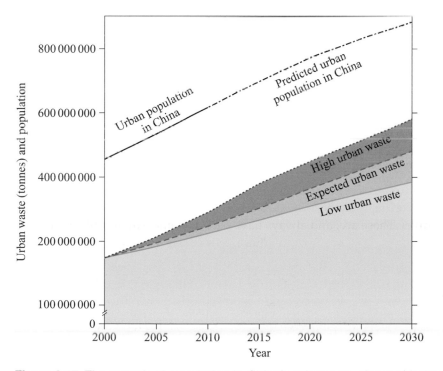

Figure 3.17 **The growth of population in China's urban area along with three different scenarios for the growth of municipal waste in China**

5.1.1   The waste waterfall in Lugu Lake

Box 3.4 is a case study of Luoshui village, which was until very recently a pristine example of a mountain village in the Yunnan province. This case study was carried out by a Chinese academic from Beijing Normal University (Tian Song, 2006) and is written from his perspective.

Box 3.4   A case study: garbage of Lugu Lake, Yunnan province

Lugu Lake (泸沽湖) is a great and beautiful lake at the boundary of Yunnan and Sichuan Province, Southeast of China. More and more tourists have visited there since the 1980s.

In October 2000, I visited Lige (里格), a small village on the shore of Lugu Lake, Yongning County, Yunnan Province, which is the habitation of the famous Mosuo people (摩梭人), or Nari people (纳日人), a branch of the Naxi ethnic group (纳西族). To my surprise, I found a garbage can in the center of the village. I lived in some small villages in northeastern China during my childhood and I never saw such things in a traditional area. In my memory, everything in villages comes from dust, and goes back to dust. Residual food could become food for chicken and pigs; garbage from home cleaning was dumped to pig beds and would later be dug out as fertilizer. I was confused by the garbage can in the village. I predicted that there must be a garbage dump outside the village, not too far, not too close. But with only a few hours to stay there, I could not ask questions such as, where do you dump your garbage?

In September 2003, I met Zhao Hua (赵画), an anthropological photographer. She took many pictures of the Nari people on the boundary of Sichuan Province and Yunnan Province. In January 2004, Zhao Hua told me that she would spend spring festival with Nari people close to Lugu Lake. I asked her to find where Lige and Luoshui (落水) dump their garbage. Luoshui is another Nari village close to Lige. It is the earliest village that developed tourism, and therefore is the richest village around Lugu Lake. It had internet bars even before 2000.

One month later, Zhao Hua called me to say that she found, and was astonished by, the garbage dumps of Lige and especially Luoshui (see Figure 3.18). For the latter, a hill several hundred meters long was covered by six years of garbage including plastic bottles, drinking packages, shoes, glass bottles and batteries. Nobody in the village visited there, nobody in the village knew how severe the garbage problem was. In my opinion, the garbage problem in Lugu Lake is the internal problem of the industrial civilization. There are no industries around Lugu Lake, so there is no industrial garbage there. But they had garbage of

Figure 3.18 (a) Waste collection truck in Luoshui village, a practice which started just a few years ago; (b) a closer look at what is in the waste stream in Luoshui; (c) cattle grazing on rotting food and waste from the informal rubbish tip. How often have you seen a plastic bag stuck in a hedgerow, tree, and shrub or along a roadside where you have travelled?; (d) the effect of an informal waste tipping process on the land and its surroundings – at the bottom of the tip, an industrious person scours the hillside for materials which can be reused, while her baby waits nearby sitting on the tip. *Source: A. Hu'aer, 2004*

the industrial civilization. When they joined the 'food chain' of modernization, the garbage problem was hardly avoidable. The garbage there had two origins: 1, that left by tourists; 2, that produced by themselves after their living standard was raised.

When they made money they became richer and richer. They used more and more industrial products in their daily lives, such as washing powder, shampoo, plastic shoes, etc., which are signs of civilization, development, progress, and so on. As a consequence, more and more nondegradable garbage appeared. The villages are the bottom of the downriver side; they can't find their own downriver for dumping their garbage, and can only dump their garbage in their own mountain. So, this case is a good illustration of my argument.

The pictures by Zhao Hua were seen by a China Central Television crew, and they asked me to help them produce a program. I hesitated at first and then agreed. Zhao Hua guided the production crew. I saw the program only when it was aired. They did not consider my explanation as given above, and still put it into a conventional pattern, that the garbage dumps were there because some officials were not duteous. After the program was broadcast, the mayor of Lijiang government asked the county government to solve the problem. The garbage hill was closed for several days, and then, the garbage disappeared from the hill. Zhao Hua guessed that the garbage was burnt and then covered by earth. Later, interesting things happened. As for Luoshui, garbage was still produced every day, but officers dared not allow dumping in the original hill. They had to find a new place. At first, they wanted to dump the garbage in the mountain of another village, but the village refused to accept it. At last, they had to dig a place the size of a basketball court, on the land of the secretary of the village, as a temporary garbage dump. Four years have passed, I plan to visit there this year and I believe that I will find a new garbage dump in the mountain close to Luoshui.

Readings taken of water visibility over a period of time in Lugu Lake can give us information about liquid garbage. Lugu Lake is very clear. In 2000 when I visited there, the visibility of the lake water was 11 meters. In 2004, when Zhao Hua visited there, the number was 9 meters. A journalist friend for Yunnan TV told me that the number was 14 meters in 1984. The lake become dirty dramatically. Since the Han dynasty, Nari people have lived around Lugu Lake. They drank lake water directly. But in 2000, I was told in Luoshui that the water close to shore was not drinkable, and people had to take a boat to the center of the lake to draw drinkable water.

(Tian Song, 2006)

These types of brownfield landfill create serious environmental problems through the contamination of the local soil and water. The sites also give off decomposing gases such as methane, a powerful greenhouse gas. Some sites also create food for wildlife which may not be the best nutritional inputs. Consider the cattle that eat plastics, for example; if you lived nearby, you might well decide to give up certain foods. But Lugu is only one of many of these stories and sites.

Some experts estimate that there are at least 5000 brownfield landfill sites in China, like the one described above, which do not have properly managed systems in place to cope with chemical spills, leachates and escaping gases. But with waste growing by some eight times between 2005 and 2020 there will need to be another new 1400 landfill sites to cope with the supply of waste, based on current solid waste plans (Hoornweg et al., 2005). Many of the current landfill sites also need urgent attention to bring their working practices up to the national sanitary standard and ensure that waste does not leak out of the site.

But there are also other, more intensive, waste sites such as that in Guiyi, which recycles electronic waste, or e-waste, and which has been labelled by some as the 'digital dump' of the world. Much of this digital rubbish (Figure 3.19) originates not in China, but overseas.

Figure 3.19 A street recycler makes a great find, as electronic equipment fetches the highest prices overall

Box 3.5 is adapted from the Basel Action Network (2002, which is cited in Hoornweg et al., 2005) and was reported again more recently to be a continuing problem.

Box 3.5   Digital dumping

Digital Dumping. Over 100 000 people active in e-waste recycling in Guiyu

Guiyu, in China, is a group of four villages lying along the Lianjiang River in the Greater Guangdong Province. An estimated 100,000 people in Guiyu are involved in the e-waste recycling business, mostly from the agrarian regions having migrated there. Recyclers on average make about $1.50 per day dismantling computers and printers, collecting toner, burning copper wires, and using fires and acid baths on circuit boards. Drinking water has been trucked into the province for several years now because some residents claim that the groundwater is foul tasting. Hundreds of trucks flow in and out of the region each day, full of scraps from printers, computers, monitors, television sets and other e-waste. The waste clearly originates from North America, but there is also scrap from Japan, Europe and South Korea. Computer shells and fragments pile up in streets, along riverbeds and in makeshift recycling villages outside of towns. Fires that melt copper wire are likely to emit hazardous gases due to the brominated flame retardants used in insulating wires. Acid-treated circuit boards lie along the riverbeds, where the groundwater was tested (in 2000) for lead and was found to be 2400 times higher than the recommended drinking water guidelines prescribed by the WHO. Pollution and waste from the electronic wastes, scrap and residues is rampant and the poor are in the main completely unprotected from the impacts.

(WMIC report, cited in Hoornweg et al., 2005)

Guiyu is not the only environmental hotspot in China due to contamination from waste but it is, like Lugu, economically motivated. Lugu profits from dumping in the environment freely, and Guiyu profits by letting chemicals seep out of very rudimentary processing plants. Looking back to Bottled Water – Who Needs It?, you can see that waste has polluted water supplies and more people have to rely on bottled water in China. But this is an environmentally unsustainable solution because of the plastic waste that is generated. The supply of bottled water also creates a form of conspicuous consumption – that is, consumption which is 'beyond' necessity in many cases. This consumption is also mirrored in the West, where we have ample potable water on tap, yet we still drink more and more bottled water, with tremendous waste consequences. As you have seen, there are different motivations for drinking bottled water, but overall the same poor environmental outcomes seem to result.

5.2   Street recycling

5.2.1   China's waste recyclers – a story of waste and bicycling

The volume and value of waste in China has generated a new wave of street-level recyclers who, in many cases, have migrated from their agricultural villages in the rural west towards the cities along the east coast. Sections 5.2.2 and 5.2.3 are based on first-hand experience by an OU environmental studies student who travelled throughout seven major cities during the months of November and December 2007 (Sinclair, 2008a and b). Fortunately for us, the student is also a photographer, and his story offers a rich visual and written picture about recycling at the street level.

The story explores how waste moves about in China and asks if there are better ways to recycle resources, and if there are any lessons we can learn from street-level recycling. It also explores the amount of waste generated in general terms each day from various households, and how the Chinese people have used the tradition of reuse of materials and the surplus of migrant labour to address the supply of waste.

5.2.2   Street recycling systems – how they operate

In many Chinese cities street recycling is a way of life, and the way it works is really quite straightforward – it is all about turning waste materials into cash for those willing to collect it. The waste provides a resource and, to some extent, a means for people to earn money to live. The individuals involved are in our Western terms self-employed entrepreneurs. If they work hard (and are lucky) they make more money than if they had not migrated from their villages. Many cities have a steady supply of materials such as paper, corrugated card, plastics and metals. From your experience, you may recognise that these are often collected for recycling (that is, making into new items with a similar function). Foam and electronic goods are also sought after. All these waste items have a cash value based on their weight. The recyclers will spend their entire day travelling around neighbourhoods collecting and buying materials. Once they have collected as much as they can carry, they then take their load to depots where the waste is weighed out and money changes hands. The recyclers buy waste materials at one price from shops and individuals and they sell them for a higher price to the depots. In many cases the people collecting waste are, not surprisingly, rural migrants who have moved towards China's coastal cities in search of a better life for themselves.

The 'bottom of the waste stream' also supplies some materials such as wood, tiles, crockery and some stone which originate from houses which have been torn down or recently abandoned in preparation for redevelopment. Street recyclers exist in many countries around the world and are called many things, including scavengers, waste pickers, informal waste collectors or cleaners (Figure 3.20). In this section I use the term recyclers, or street recyclers, as their occupation is focused on getting materials which have a market value that can be sold on to be reused in some format. The majority of their activity takes place at the street level and in many cases the recyclers do not venture much further than their neighbourhood area.

Figure 3.20 A woman collecting paper and cardboard in an area which is being cleared for housing redevelopment. These projects rely partly on street recycling to ensure that a significant amount of waste is recovered

One of the largest waste streams in terms of waste generation is the general rubble produced during demolition. Some of this rubble, such as 'hardcore' (i.e. broken bricks, rocks, etc.) can be used again as a base or infill for new building sites, depending on its quality and content. Wood, as shown in Figure 3.21, along with other household items, is also generated, along with copious quantities of dust. Demolition reveals iron and steel from concrete-encrusted reinforcing bars, and this can be melted down and used again.

Figure 3.21 Old Shanghai hutong being cleared for new high-rise buildings

There is also the issue of waste statistics and how much waste there actually is versus how much a government may report. Like levels of crime, many governments only know the exact number of car thefts when all thefts are accurately reported – an unreported effect. Also, as governments collect more data about more things, the process in some cases becomes more reliable and robust. There is likely to be quite a lot of waste which is generated but not necessarily collected, or not counted in the collection process (Hoornweg et al., 2005). The key point is that we may never know the exact amount of waste generated from a city, but we can be fairly certain that it seems to be growing, and that the only way to really know the final waste figures is to study the situation in further depth.

5.2.3   By foot, two wheels and three wheels

There is a social hierarchy within the recycling community, with the lowest tier involving people on foot collecting what they can carry. These are inevitably the very poorest of the recyclers. They will generally be reasonably able-bodied people, although often with some physical disability. People with birth defects or other impairments are typically among the poorest people you come across on China's streets. People from this group will have either chosen not to beg or will have learned that they can earn more from recycling than from begging. Begging in any case can only be a very last resort in China, as the Chinese tend to give only to beggars who are manifestly not able to work for a living (often very old people or others with disabilities or injuries).

As they have only very limited resources, the pedestrian recyclers tend to collect their materials from waste bins rather than buying it from others. Coming from a Western liberal background, where social provision is something that many of us might assume will always be there, the sight of such poor people collecting packaging and also discarded food from bins can be very upsetting. However, either this group is relatively small or it is less visible, as most of the recyclers you see are poor rather than destitute. The next tier above are those people who carry their materials on bicycles, and the next level up from them use tricycle rickshaws (see Figure 3.22). Of the on-street recyclers I observed, the tricyclers are clearly the most prosperous. They can carry more and benefit from economies of scale in terms of the number of trips to depots. Often you will see two people working together on one tricycle and this team work may help them to support each other throughout the day.

The tricycles can carry much more waste and these recyclers can then achieve more trips per day in theory, and potentially earn more money. In China's bustling streets it is easy to overlook the recyclers at work. The ubiquitous tricycle is used for an extraordinary range of activities; it can be a taxi, a delivery vehicle, a mobile eatery, a shop or a workshop. However, if you have ever been to China's cities, or are ever there, you will soon

Figure 3.22 Slightly wealthier street recyclers advertising their services on the front of the tricycles in the city of Hangzhou; their scales can be seen in the bike basket on the left

realise how common an activity recycling is in many districts. Many of the tricycle fronts have impromptu signs attached to them offering recycling services to the general public. These signs typically say that they are especially looking for electronic equipment, wires and metals, as these items command the highest values in the depots in terms of making a profit. The two men in Figure 3.22 were in fact working together as a team in order to combine their recycled loads and then split their earning equally. His sign translates as 'I buy (I recycle) air conditioners, refrigerators, TVs, etc.' as these items command more money from the recycling depots. Sometimes recyclers work in pairs or small groups if there are especially bulky or heavy loads that need to be moved. A typical day of work for street recyclers results in a take home pay of approximately £2 per day, or less.

Generally, solid residential waste can be categorised into many broad areas, as shown in Table 3.6. Household waste is considered more complex than industrial and agricultural waste simply because it contains a much more complex variety of items. Industrial waste streams tend be narrower in their components, but not necessarily easier to treat. In terms of solid waste from the various Chinese municipalities, each item has a corresponding price which the buyers pay to the residents to obtain. The recycling depots then hopefully pay more for the waste resources, and this is how the collectors make their earnings.

The items listed in Table 3.6 range from those recyclables that make the most money (copper) to those worth the least (glass, timber and used pieces of furniture). Considering that many street recyclers make some $2–4 per day, you can see that it takes multiple heavy loads each day of typical rubbish consisting of paper and cardboard (Figure 3.23) to match the profit that could be gained from one large load of scrap wiring. Obviously, as prices of these commodities fluctuate in the market, this in turn means that the earnings of each collector also go up and down.

Table 3.6 Recyclables and their average prices in Beijing	
Recyclables	**Price ($US per kg) paid to residents**
Copper	3.33
Brass (copper and zinc)	1.93
Alnico (aluminium/nickel/cobalt alloys)	1.56
Soft drink cans	1.12
Plastic water bottles	0.73
Plastic soft drink bottles	0.57
Plastic cooking oil bottles	0.45
Plastic	0.31
Steel	0.22
Paper	0.15
Books	0.14
Chipboard	0.10
Glass bottles	0.04
Timber	0.02
Used furniture/machine	*

Adapted from Wang et al., 2008.

*The price of used furniture varies as it may be sold on in a secondary market and refurbished rather than being recycled as timber or broken into its component pieces.

Figure 3.23   A cardboard collection depot in a very desirable area in Hong Kong. It might be hard to imagine such an image in London, where land values are very much higher

Activity 3.3   Exploring uncollected household wastes in China

What types of household-generated solid wastes do you think might be missing from Table 3.6, and why?

Discussion

I noted that textiles, batteries and hazardous wastes were not mentioned in the table, and I began to think about why this might be. Disposal of these things was either specialist or dangerous or, in the case of rags, perhaps not profitable. Rags (or used clothing items) also seem to be missing from the table, and considering the demand for used clothing in the UK this might come as a surprise. Perhaps it is due to the fact that the majority of people in China use their clothing items much longer than in the Western world and continue to reuse them in some other form in the household (for rags, cleaning or stuffing) rather than sell them on as a commodity. You may well have thought of other equally relevant items.

Batteries are certainly one thing not shown in Table 3.6, despite being recyclable and containing useful resource materials. Batteries, however, are also difficult to recycle and in many cases contain both solid and liquid components. When batteries rupture or are broken they can leak acid into their surrounding environment. There are also no hazardous wastes listed, such as pesticides or chemicals or paints. Again these probably require some type of disposal permit or specialist knowledge. For paints or pesticides, perhaps these items are in such demand that there is virtually no waste generated as nearly all of the product gets applied or utilised fully.

When you have completed Activity 3.3 you may want to try Activity 3.4 now or when you reach the end of the part.

Activity 3.4   Waste habits

You have now read about two very different waste situations, that in Lugu Lake (Box 3.4) and that of recycling at the street level in most major cities in China (Section 5.2). Compare and contrast both situations with respect to the principles in the waste hierarchy (Box 3.3). How do either of these cases compare with your own household waste habits and what your local council, city or area offers?

Discussion

The first is as in the village case study, whereby the villagers simply dump their waste on a mountain (or in an 'informal landfill'). The second, as demonstrated by the street recyclers, is to make a business out of garbage and treat the unwanted waste as potentially useful materials to be re-fed into another production stream (Figures 3.24 (a) and (b)). The first possibly echoes our own previous historical approach, the second what we are being encouraged to aim for in terms of reuse within the waste hierarchy. The street recyclers also demonstrate differentiation of recycling – some collect plastic, others metal etc. My city has black bins for landfill waste, green bins for compostable waste (including a wide range of meat-related wastes and cardboard/paper) along with plastic, glass and paper recycling. Our council requires us to recycle and tries to encourage people to use less if possible by providing information about waste generated each year. I have heard that some councils are considering charging for waste by weighing it but I have not seen this in action yet.

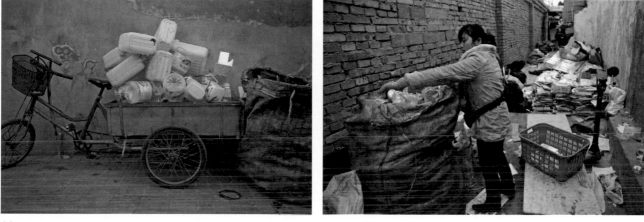

(a)   (b)

Figure 3.24 (a) A tricycle about to be unloaded at an impromptu recycling depot in Beijing. The depot is collecting plastic bottles and other plastic items for recycling and transporting them to the factory in very large plastic mesh bags (on the right). (b) Ad hoc recycling centre in an alley. This recycler is sorting items and weighing the plastics using the scale on the right-hand side of the picture

Many recycling systems all over the world use similar ways of sorting waste for reuse. A snapshot of 19 European countries, along with 12 other countries, is shown in Table 3.7; this gives an indication of the type and level of materials that get recycled.

Although not shown here, it is clear that much of our own rubbish ends up elsewhere for reprocessing, whether it be plastic, paper or e-waste. In the case of the UK, China takes about half of our paper, and 80% of recovered plastics (WRAP, 2008). In terms of overall CO_2 emissions, even when transport to China is included it is much better to recycle overseas than to use 'new' material to produce virgin plastics. This argument is further strengthened by the import–export imbalance for countries like the UK and China, whereby some ships leaving the UK might otherwise be empty.

Recycling in China at best provides little more than subsistence at the street level, and to generate a living requires working seven days a week in all weathers. Many Chinese, especially from this group of ex-peasant farmers turned recyclers, have recent memories of very hard times indeed. As you saw in earlier parts of this block, their lives were afflicted by natural disasters such as famines, droughts or flooding as well as the impact of living under a centralised economy. Undoubtedly, economic liberalisation

Table 3.7 Municipal waste generated and waste treatment rates from selected countries

Country	Annual waste generated (kg per person)	Landfilled (%)	Incinerated (%)	Recycled (%)	Composted (%)
Belgium	492	4	34	39	23
Czech Republic	294	84	13	2	1
Denmark	801	5	53	24	17
Germany	564	1	35	46	18
Ireland	786	64	0	34	2
Greece	448	84	0	14	2
Spain	588	60	10	13	17
France	541	34	36	16	14
Italy	550	46	11	11	33
Cyprus	754	87	0	13	0
Luxembourg	694	25	47	0	28
Hungary	456	77	9	13	1
Malta	652	93	0	2	5
Netherlands	630	3	38	32	28
Austria	597	13	28	21	38
Portugal	472	63	19	8	10
Romania	379	99	0	1	0
Sweden	518	4	47	37	12
United Kingdom	572	57	9	22	12
EU27 (average)	522	42	20	22	17
United States	750	54	14	24	8
Japan	426	3	74	17	0
Rep. of Korea	380	36	14	49	0
China	115	43	3	–	5
Australia	445	70	0	30	0
Canada	416	73	–	27	13
Brazil	328	63	< 1	1	4
Cuba	392	84	0	5	11
Iceland	499	72	9	16	9
Lebanon	375	42	–	3	8
Niger	722	64	12	4	–
Singapore	1153	16	45	39	0

Notes: EU27 data for year 2007. Not all values add to 100% because of rounding errors. A dash indicates that data was not reported for these sources.

Sources: For EU27 countries see Europa, 2009

For other countries (2000–2005) see United Nations Statistics Division, 2009 has created much opportunity in China; people now have choices that they never had before, and even among people whose life looks hard to us there is a belief among most street recyclers that things are getting better. As wealth and consumption grow in China, then the overall levels of waste generation and energy consumption must also surely increase. This growth at the potential expense of their environment and, by extension, our environment, is undoubtedly one of the great challenges facing both those in China and those of us 'outside' of China.

Summary of Section 5

China's enormous increase in manufacturing has brought with it an increase in the output of wastes. These arise not only from the production process but also during the use of the products by consumers. Depending on where and how these wastes are deposited, they may just be dumped, creating pollution problems. But in urban China, a separate industry has grown up around the recovery of wastes to be used as raw materials. Waste management is an increasing need worldwide, and understanding the hierarchy of wastes, as well as the overall global flows of goods and wastes, helps with this process.

6 Red, black and green dragons

In the previous sections we considered the extraordinary economic growth of China which has pushed the country into becoming a new world force shaping both China and the world outside China. In this conclusion I consider three simplified possible alternative futures – called red, black and green dragons – for China, based on what you have already learned within the course, and particularly about China and the global environment. I have tried to choose colours that have associations with the general form of each imagined future. The dragon has long been a symbol in many places, but in China the dragon brings water and thus prosperity to the places it adorns, such as the Hall of Supreme Harmony within the Forbidden City (Zijincheng) in the heart of Beijing.

In fact the word dragon, in the English language, is an incorrect translation of the Chinese word loong, one of which is shown in the figure below. In essence the three scenarios ought to be entitled the three loongs rather than dragons as the two are not interchangeable. A dragon, such as the one featured in the flag of Wales, or in stories about St. George, is very different indeed to a loong. Dragons have wings, breathe fire and generally speaking are fairly nasty creatures, which tend to be popularised by their habit of eating people. Loong on the other hand do not have wings and are symbols of power, prosperity and good luck (see Figure 3.25) – the body of a loong

Figure 3.25 Typical loong sculpture in China

is long and slender, rather than being stocky like the dragon. If you have ever seen a loong dance, sometimes mistakenly called the Chinese dragon dance, during Chinese New Year's festivals, then you may recall that these are long processions, usually gold in colour, with red highlights and very auspicious. Loong don't eat people, but they do represent a god of water and through this symbolism promote the well-being of all humankind. In this sense our scenarios should not be called loongs at all, as the idea of a black loong to most Chinese would be quite disturbing. Thus, it is probably quite appropriate for us to use our rather 'Western' frame of thought and stick with dragons for our section titles; just make sure you don't confuse a dragon with a loong!

The black dragon represents a focus on economic growth as the main driver of policy. In China it is frequently the colour chosen for young boys' clothing and has always been associated with the north, the winter and water. Black as a colour is also known to cancel out anything, or any other colour, which is lighter than itself. In contrast to many Western traditions, white is worn to funerals in China, although this is changing slowly towards a preference for black.

The green dragon vision represents a shift towards placing environmental issues at the heart of their policies and energy. In China, green can be used to represent the colour of wood, which gives rise to fire (red), as depicted in the ancient Chinese elements.

The red dragon form signals a return towards the old China, with the hierarchical control that dominated many people, by the few, creating multiple tensions. In the red version, the Party directs what happens; the results could be green or black, and the issue is whether individual freedom should take precedence.

Remember that with any predictions and forecasts we are bound to get at least part of it incorrect, and that many unexpected twists are likely. Equally probable are dragons of other colours and thus we would do well to keep in mind the saying that 'not everything is black and white'.

Black dragon

My image of the black dragon, with growth at all costs, is quite bleak, particularly with high environmental costs as depicted in the excerpt below.

> 'These days,' says Pan Yue, China's deputy minister for the environment, 'most Chinese missions go abroad to talk about securing energy, whereas most foreign missions come to China to talk about our environmental impact. It's a paradoxical diplomacy.'
>
> For China's neighbours, the country poses an environmental threat on several levels. In late 2005 an explosion at a chemical plant in north-eastern Jilin province sent a slick of toxic benzene 80 km long into the Songhua River. Local authorities attempted a cover-up, but the city of Harbin was forced to shut down its water supply. With Russia downstream, the spill became an international incident.
>
> *(The Economist, 2007)*

A black China would place economic growth as its main thrust of policy. Individual economic decisions would continue to produce a strong migration shift to feed the urban production systems supplying their wares. The drivers of personal wealth and consumption, and their associated outcomes of continued exploitation of the biophysical environment, treating land etc. as an inexhaustible source of resources/unfillable sink for pollution, would continue for some time to come. But this may be what the majority want. And it certainly seems to be what most of the West wants, being able to 'sweep our externalities under the Chinese carpet'.

Green dragon

With the green dragon vision we might predict a strong course towards resource conservation, waste reduction and consumption which is not conspicuous, but a course that depended on guidance rather than central control. A China which was 'green' would be more conscious of its own consumption and it might, for example, place a strong emphasis on green taxation for energy-hungry devices. All appliances might become regulated by law to be A-rated for lowest possible energy consumption, both when running and when in stand-by mode. Stand-by mode might be eliminated altogether. Smart appliances might run when electricity is readily available on the grid, with dishes and clothes being washed late at night on very slow, low energy-drawing cycles. High fuel consumption vehicles, like 4×4s and 'muscle cars' and SUVs – sports utility vehicles – might be given very high taxation to discourage purchasing and use. Wooden chopsticks would be taxed to encourage reuse of plastic ones with lower overall life cycle costs in terms of resource and energy use (East, 2006).

A green dragon would consider a path into the future based on reducing their coal extraction and overall coal consumption in their energy mix to less than 40% by 2030 (Coonan, 2006). The conservation of the environment would be placed before production and economic targets, with new national goals such as targets for water recycling, minimum water usage and programmes promoting forest growth and control of soil erosion wherever possible. Within the green scenario China might not be the richest country in the world, but it would continue to grow, albeit more slowly, and spread its wealth in a more equitable way. A green China would lift even more Chinese people out of poverty by providing life choices through education and health benefits for all. Sustainability within schools would become a major pillar in the curriculum, causing a large shift in teaching and learning across all generations. A more sustainable China would also consider how to balance the need for jobs in the urban area, to maintain growth, along with ways to counteract negative outcomes associated with mass migration. Food consumption, both in diet make-up and quantity, could be curbed. Although the green dragon might sound idyllic there would still be much hardship and upheaval, with unexpected events from past excesses. Below is a short quote that emphasises some of the events which might be seen as leading us towards a green dragon future.

When Hu Jintao became president of China in 2003, his administration carefully examined the trajectory of China's industrial and urban development. Since then a new policy emphasis on 'harmony between man and nature' and on 'building a conservation oriented and environmentally friendly society' has emerged. China's political leaders started to insist that 'economic development must consider its impact on the environment and on society'. Speaking at the 2004 Asian-Pacific Economic Cooperation (APEC) CEO Summit in Santiago, President Hu exclaimed, 'The historical experience of human progress shows that we should never seek development at the cost of wasting resources and damaging the environment. Otherwise mankind will have to pay a high price and ultimately the development itself will be threatened. Development should proceed along the road of high technological content, sound economic efficiency, low resource consumption, little environmental pollution and full use of human resources.'

He went one step further, however, in his 2007 speech at the 17th Party Congress setting out the new 5 year plan. Here, for the first time, he referred to 'moving China towards an ecological civilisation with much more efficient use of resources and use of renewable energy'. He cited the need for research, new services and an emphasis on design. He referred to the development of a circular economy through the new law, controlling emissions and improving the environment. This is an important example of national leadership recognising that growth following the industrial model will become uneconomic because of environmental and health costs and rising raw material costs.

(Head, 2009, p. 12)

But whatever the colour of the dragon, not all of the indicators and issues in a future scenario can be easily pigeonholed into a simple category. There would invariably be elements of both black and green. We may see the old capitalist markets continuing in some areas in their business as usual guise (that is to say, further economic growth at all costs), but we should expect the inevitable surprises. These might include a strong willingness to reduce greenhouse gases once a very robust system is in place for emissions trading, which may drive down the overall emissions in the long term. Other surprises may occur when certain systems, or even whole economies, fail, but then after some time the world might realise that it can get along without those systems or economies.

One point that is perhaps inherent in both black and green scenarios is that if enough people can be persuaded to believe in some entity, be it a god, 'the economy' or something else, then rational discussion of that entity seems to get curtailed, and those who have access to media can persuade the general public of the need for whatever action benefits that entity. In the black scenario, growth of 'the economy' is unchallengeable, and all actions are judged against the growth that they can allow. What if, instead of the economy being dominant, 'the environment' was what had to grow at all costs? Is this what underlies the green dragon? These are big philosophical questions, and a lifetime of study could be devoted to these issues, which are not simply semantic. This course, and this block in particular, can only begin to open up the debate, and we sincerely hope you will continue to ask yourself what is truly sustainable, under what conditions, and why.

Red dragon

The image of a red dragon might be used to depict 'red' as both a warning that things are in danger in our Western view, but perhaps too that China must have a solution that is ultimately and uniquely Chinese. It, as a framework, prioritises placing Chinese values against all other ideologies, and so may incorporate some elements from both green and black scenarios. For example, a black dragon may harbour a distinct streak of green; this may be borne out of what we have seen as the discontent of many Chinese people. Their efforts and energy may be turned towards a new social movement to protect and promote nature with the backing of some industries. In fact the emphasis on saving and reducing waste is so great, even in the 'black' future, that waste is being virtually eradicated. This is a result of high land values forcing many landfill sites to close and new job creation in waste-related industries. Instead, energy from waste becomes big business, and a new breed of Chinese designers rises up, completely dedicated to products embodied with low material usage, with low energy requirements. Red has been a noted colour of China for many centuries, signalling prosperity and happiness. There has been much talk, both hype and some action, about the greening of the dragon, but a red dragon would see a return to the old control of a strong central government, with power wielded by a few, but just possibly to the good of many. A red future could show signs of fortune and of revolution. Green and black dragons are based on different ethics, a consumerist ethic (black) and in the green, an environmental ethic. The one 'solution' to this green–black dilemma could be the uniquely Chinese red version, where the Party keeps much more control over what happens. The outcome then depends on what the Party decides, and the Party could order environmentally friendly actions. But as you have seen before, not everyone agrees with what the Party decides. This could then lead to the sorts of conflicts and caveats you read about earlier in the block. If we turn again to the main economic framework used for this block, then perhaps we ought to consider the value of our environment.

Many economists have recognised the importance of attempting to place values on the environment, which can be extremely difficult to do. It has given rise to a new branch called ecological economics, which Head describes with the following metaphor:

> [...]...has emerged in which the Earth is seen as a ship and the gross material production of the economy as its cargo. In this model the economists say we do not yet know how heavy a load is safe but we know, in principle, that too heavy a load will cause the ship to sink. This discipline has been emerging in the academic world for 20 years and it is clear that economic growth must eventually be replaced by sustainable development in which human development continues without continual increased use of resources.

(Head, 2009, p. 13)

A red, green or black dragon will ultimately fail if the overall level of understanding of sustainability is not incorporated into everything we do. What good would any economic growth be, as measured in terms of GDP per capita, if we did not also have a measure and target for ensuring that the wellbeing of all citizens also increased? This kind of question should help us decide which metrics are best for following a sustainable pathway by using a wide variety of indicators to guide and shape our decisions. As Part 1 discussed, these issues raise the question of governance. Although the future trajectory of the planet depends on individual decisions, these are informed or curtailed by governance structures. Do we stick with the 'Western' theory of an informed electorate choosing a government that enables the wishes of the majority to be fulfilled, which could lead to green or black scenarios depending on how those wishes are shaped and interpreted? The shaping factors include all kinds of influences such as education, media and language. This is where indicators are important, providing alternatives to the dominance of the single indicator of GDP in both the West and in post-1979 China. Considering a wider range of indicators should change the discourse, as discussed in Block 1. But there is no guarantee that this will succeed in producing sustainability either. So should we look to a much more state-controlled (red) model, where some higher body (the Party) directs what people do? An environmentally active Chinese Communist Party could ensure sustainability if it decided that it was in its interests, or in the national interest, to do so, simply by directing resources in the appropriate way. But would that state control model be acceptable globally? And how might such a Communist Party interact with the rest of the world? Because of China's unique history and governance there is some possibility that the red dragon might just rise up and become a more powerful scenario than we had previously imagined.

I don't think there is any argument! Continued growth for a minority of the world population at the expense of many raises many complex ethical issues. The quote above, concerning ecological economics, should also make us realise that there are many areas of academic expertise that are simply not yet known, or are still very young. This lack of knowledge and expertise means that we are not and will not always be knowledgeable enough to make the more sustainable choices. Whichever dragon emerges in the future will be a surprise in some ways, and it is likely that we will only know the best course of action with hindsight, some time after the event.

Summary of Part 3

We cannot predict with any certainty which path China will take in its future development, and these very basic scenarios should not be taken too seriously, despite some of the serious issues within each one. I have created them purposely to encourage you to consider potential consequences that may happen, and to think deeply about some actions that you, the state, civil society and the market can take to become more sustainable. Each of these is responsible for advancing sustainability and placing the environment at the focus of its priorities. Yet at the same time I have tried to highlight the importance of the constructed and imprecise nature of the term 'the environment' and in general the idea of becoming more sustainable. We are so accustomed to hearing talk of 'the economy' that we assume it must have some clear and agreed form. You might like to examine some news reports in different media to see how often this occurs. How often do phrases like 'keeping the economy growing' or 'the cost to the economy is $xx million', as though the economy has some objective existence. But the idea of the economy is just that; it is an idea or model that has been useful. We should not let it determine how we think about almost everything. Maybe we should be talking about 'the environment' as if it were some equally objective entity, that by analogy with 'the economy' has to be kept growing, or healthy, or stable. How would our actions change if this were to have equal prominence to statements about the economy? Of course, in some cases we simply don't know what is best in terms of environmental choices and decisions. As you will have seen by now, both in the course and hopefully elsewhere, the sustainability 'bandwagon' has been used by many, and in many cases misused by many too. As I close the block I now want you to again turn towards yourself, away from China, and consider: what does this mean for you personally? Just as China is changing and will continually change, your world around you will change, continuously, and present changes in the form of environmental challenges. These challenges can ultimately be met only by a combination of action from both individuals and governments.

After completing Part 3 you should be able to:

- understand how current 'Western' lifestyles and aspirations lead to increased consumption
- appreciate how resources are used to form products and how product creation also leads to waste and undesired outputs
- explain and illustrate the waste hierarchy and its role in both informal and formal waste management systems

- use life cycle analysis on a simplified basis to describe impacts for the production and use of products
- recognise that economic valuation does not provide an appropriate measure of all the consequences of human actions
- appreciate the environmental implications of consumer behaviour.

As individuals, it may often seem that our actions are insignificant in terms of their effect on our global environment. Examining what is happening in China should remind us that while we are all individuals, there are about 6.8 billion of us in the world, and if we all make similar decisions, the total effect is potentially enormous. On its own your larger, more comfortable, but less fuel-efficient car may be a trivial contributor to climate change. But if, as is the case, everyone in China seems to aspire to owning a car or owning a bigger and better one, then we can see how the outcome is not going to be trivial. Because China's industrial system allows for the production of consumer goods at a low price, we are all tempted to buy more and consume more. Seeing the resulting problems that the wastes from this consumption cause when concentrated in China should at least make us think, and when multiplied by the millions in China making similar decisions, that cheap burger can have negative impacts on Amazonian forests. If working through this block has made you more conscious of these effects and more likely to think about your decisions, then the authors can feel pleased.

Answers to SAQs

SAQ 3.1

For plastics, this is 266 370 tonnes imported from China which, when converted to kilograms and divided by the population 59 700 000 to get per person values, yields 4.5 kg per person. Similarly for toys it is 6.3 kg per person. These values are obviously higher per household: 10.2 kg plastics per household and 14.5 kg toys per household. Obviously one needs to be careful with this type of generalisation as there is no such thing as a typical household, and toy content we might suspect is dependent on the number of children in the family.

SAQ 3.2

Urban ownership is always higher than rural, with approximate values of 120 and 50, respectively. In urban homes the average number of colour TVs per 100 households exceeded 100 TVs. This means that some households started to own more than one TV. Conversely, it is equally likely that there are some households which don't own a TV at all, so without being able to see the complete data set we don't know the full story, but it is clear that rural home ownership levels are about 10–12 years 'behind' those of urban homes.

SAQ 3.3

The arguments against bottled water could include any of the following: economically wasteful, poor use of water resources, using plastic/energy (oil, etc.) to make/transport/dispose of bottles, could be considered a greenhouse gas contributor (e.g. bottled water has a much higher CO_2 cost than tap water), and it might promote a certain type of lifestyle (whether right or wrong). There is also an argument which might be considered – a social and ethical one – if by bottling water we are depriving others of their own water sources, or if we are endangering wildlife.

Arguments for bottled water could include jobs for those in the plastic industry, and products for those travelling. You may have thought of other equally valid arguments for both cases.

SAQ 3.4

The water consumption for the shirt would be 50 washes per year multiplied by 3 years, to get a total of 150 washes. Each wash uses 40 litres, so three years of washing is equivalent to 6000 litres. Some things you might have noted are: there is a need to account for the laundry soap, dealing with waste water and supplying energy. Further impacts could be counted when the washing machine needs disposal. Also not accounted for here is the fact that most machines can take a load of 3–5 kg (of dry clothing) and a shirt probably only weighs 500 grams or less, thus a more accurate or sensible approach would consider water use per load washed.

References

BBC Online (2008) 'Corruption 'threatens China rainforest'', http://news.bbc.co.uk/1/hi/7570501.stm 21 August 2008 (Accessed 20 October 2009).

BP Statistical Review (2008) 'Statistical Review of World' June 2009, BP, http://www.bp.com/liveassets/bp_internet/globalbp/globalbp_uk_english/reports_and_publications/statistical_energy_review_2008/STAGING/local_assets/2009_downloads/statistical_review_of_world_energy_full_report_2009.pdf (Accessed 1 October 2009).

Chapagain, A.G., Hoekstra, A.Y., Savenije, H.H.G. and Gautam, R. (2006) 'The water footprint of cotton consumption: an assessment of impact of worldwide consumption of cotton products on the water resources in the cotton producing countries', *Ecological Economics*, vol. 60, pp. 186–203.

China Statistical Yearbook (2005) http://www.stats.gov.cn/tjsj/ndsj/2005/indexee.htm (Accessed 7 October 2009).

Coonan, C. (2006) 'Energy in the hothouse', in *Greening the Dragon – China's Search For a Sustainable Future*, A Green Futures Special Supplement, Green Futures, no. 60, Sept–Oct, pp. 8–10.

Croll, E. (2006) *China's New Consumers, Social Development and Domestic Demand*, Oxford, Routledge.

Defra (2008) *Environmental Permitting*, Department for Environment, Food and Rural Affairs, London.

EarthTrends (2005) 'Carbon dioxide emissions by source 2005 (CDIAC and WRI)', *Data Tables: climate and atmosphere*, pp. 1–5, http://earthtrends.wri.org/pdf_library/data_tables/cli3_2005.pdf (Accessed 3 August 2009).

East, R. (2006) 'Sifting myths from mountains on the long green march', in *Greening the Dragon – China's Search For a Sustainable Future*, A Green Futures Special Supplement, Green Futures, no. 60, Sept–Oct, pp. 5–7.

EIU Country Profile (2007) Country report, China. Economist Intelligence Unit, New York.

Energy Watch Group (2007) 'Coal: resources and future production', Energy Watch Group, March 2007, EWG-Series No 1/2007. http://www.energywatchgroup.org/fileadmin/global/pdf/EWG_Report_Coal_10-07-2007ms.pdf (Accessed 1 October 2009).

Europa (2009) 'Municipal waste', http://europa.eu/rapid/pressReleasesAction.do?reference=STAT/09/31&format=HTML&aged=0&language=EN&guiLanguage=en (Accessed 7 October 2009).

Gleick, P.H. (2009) *The World's Water 2008–2009*, with Heather Cooley, Michael J. Cohen, Mari Morikawa, Jason Morrison, and Meena Palaniappan, Island Press, pp. 335–8.

Head, P. (2009) 'Entering the ecological age: the engineer's role', *Brunel International Lectures*, pp. 12–13. http://www.arup.com/~/media/Files/PDF/Publications/Research_and_whitepapers/Ecological_Age/EngineersRole.ashx (Accessed 7 October 2009).

Hoornweg, D., Lam, P. and Chaudhry, M. (2005) 'Waste management in China: issues and recommendations', May, http://siteresources.worldbank.org/INTEAPREGTOPURBDEV/Resources/China-Waste-Management1.pdf (Accessed 3 August 2009).

McKibben, B. (2009) 'Our energy challenge', Energy for tomorrow: repowering the planet, special issue, *National Geographic*, March, pp. 24–31.

Navarro, P. (2007) 'Deconstructing the China Price', *The Economists' Voice*, February, pp. 1–4, http://www.bepress.com/ev/vol4/iss1/art5/ (Accessed 3 August 2009).

OECD (2005) OECD Economic Surveys, China.

Official Journal of the European Union (2008) Directive on Waste and Repealing Certain Directives. 2008/98/EC, L312: 3-30.

Simms, A., Johnson, V. and Smith, J. (2007) *Chinadependence, The Second UK Interdependence Report*, London, New Economics Foundation and The Open University.

Sinclair, N. (2008a), 'Recycling, poverty and climate change', Final Report to Winston Churchill Memorial Trust travel fellowship to Hong Kong and China, February 2008, 25 pp.

Sinclair, N. (2008b) *Megacycle*, Blurb Publishing, 160 pp. See http://www.blurb.com/bookstore/detail/432956

The Economist (2007) 'Grim tales: Reaching for a renaissance – a special report on China and its region', by Dominic Ziegler, *The Economist,* vol. 382, no. 8522.

The Economist (2008) 'Why China is not to blame for the surge in global inflation', 16 August, vol. 388, no. 8593, p. 72.

Tian Song (2006) 'Why can you drink a bottle of mineral water at any street corner of any urban?: the transformation chain of matter and energy of the global in the age of limited earth', *Chinese Book Review Monthly*, vol. 1, pp. 18–21.

United Nations Statistics Division (2009) 'Municipal waste treatment', http://unstats.un.org/unsd/environment/wastetreatment.htm (Accessed 7 October 2009).

Wagner, H.-J. (2008) *Energy: the World's Race for Resources in the 21st Century*, (translated by P. Hill). Haus Publishing, London, p. 48.

Wagner, L.A. (2001) 'Materials in the economy – material flows, scarcity, and the environment', US Department of the Interior, US Geological Survey, US Geological Survey Circular 1221.

Wang, Jing (2008) *Brand New China: Advertising, Media and Commercial Culture*, Cambridge, Massachusetts, Harvard University Press.

Wang, J., Han, L. and Li, S. (2008) 'The collection system for residential recyclables in communities in Haidian District, Beijing: a possible approach for China recycling', *Waste Management*, vol. 28, pp. 1672–80.

Winters, L.A. and Yusuf, S. (eds) (2007) *Dancing with Giants – China, India, and the Global Economy*, copublication International Bank for Reconstruction and Development/The Work Bank, Washington DC, and The Institute of Policy Studies, Singapore.

World Energy Outlook (2007), *China and India Insights*, Paris, International Energy Agency and Organisation for Economic Co-operation and Development.

WRAP (2008) 'CO_2 impacts of transporting the UK's recovered paper and plastic bottles to China', Waste and Resources Action Programme, final report, August 2008, 28 pp. http://www.wrap.org.uk/downloads/CO2_Impact_of_Export_Report_v8_1Aug08.e8b35f0d.5760.pdf (Accessed 7 October 2009).

Ziegler, D. (2007) 'Reaching for a renaissance – a special report on China and its region', *The Economist*, vol. 382, no. 8522, 31 March.

Acknowledgements

Acknowledgements are due to Nick Sinclair, Professor Tian Song, and all those who helped contribute to the case studies and stories used in the Block.

Grateful acknowledgement is made to the following sources:

Text

Gerin, R.(2009) The Rising Cost of Rubber, Beijing Review, March 19th 2009;

Courtesy of http://thelandfarmonline.com.au. Rural Press;

Expanding deserts in China forcing farmers from fields sending sandstorms across Pacific (2007) From http://english.sina.com/china. Used with permission of The Associated Press Copyright © 2009. All rights reserved;

Hauer, A. (2004) Seminar paper: The Ecological Civilization Imperative in the Age of Limited Earth. Why can we drink a bottle of mineral water on any street corner of any city?

Tables

Table 1.3: Central Intelligence Agency, Washington, USA;

Table 2.2: Buck, J.L. (1930) *Chinese Farm Economy*, The University of Chicago Press;

Table 2.4: Mottram, R.F. (1979) Human Nutrition, Edward Arnold;

Table 2.5: Paul, A.A. and Southgate, D.A.T. (1978) *McCance & Widdowson's The Composition of Foods*, HMSO;

Table 2.6: Croll, E. (1983) *The Family Rice Bowl*, Zed Books Ltd;

Table 3.2: From Simms et al. (2007) Chinadependence: The second UK Interdependence Report, New Economics Foundation/The Open University and www.tradeinfo.com;

Tables 3.3 and 3.4: Croll, E. (2006) China's new consumers, social development and domestic demand, Routledge;

Table 3.7: Adapted from Troschinetz (2009) Waste Management, Elsevier.

Figures

Figure 1.4: Adapted from Fan, C. (2008) *China on the Move*, Routledge using Mountain High Maps ® Copyright © 1993 Digital Wisdom Inc.; Figure 1.7: © Forrest Anderson/Getty Images; Figure 1.8: © Andrew McConnell/Alamy; Figure 1.9: © Peter Bowater/Alamy; Figure 1.10: © Sovfoto; Figure 1.12: © Panos Pictures; Figure 1.13: © Anne-Cecile Gutlman; Figure 1.15: © Rhodri Jones/Panos Pictures; Figure 1.16: © Reuters; Figure 1.17: © Getty Images; Figure 1.18: © Press Association Images; Figure 1.19: From http://i92.photobucket.com; Figure 1.20: © Trygve Bolstad/Panos Pictures; Figure 1.21: © Google Inc.;